MAGENTA'S TARTAN SOCKS

Written by Nikki Johnston
Illustrated by Mitch Vane

Magenta had tartan socks,
with checks of brilliant crimson and powerful purple.
Magenta had frilly knickers,
with frivolous lace and little flowery bits.
Magenta had spangly bangles,
with sparkles of sapphire and splashes of silver.

Magenta also had a little brother.

One proud and glorious day,
Magenta wore her tartan socks down the street.

"Oh, my!" remarked a lady,
with a Pekingese dangling from her wrist.
"Wherever did you get such truly terrific tartan socks?"

And Magenta said,
  "My Nana brought them back for me,
From far away, across the sea.
She sludged through swamps and climbed a tree
To bring these socks back home for me."

The lady said, "Oh, really?"

But Magenta's little brother said,
"She did not, Magenta.
She bought them at the shop."

On another proud and glorious day,
Magenta wore her frilly knickers down the street.

"Oh, my!" remarked a girl,
with a turtle trailing behind.
"Wherever did you get such
frightfully fancy and frilly knickers?"

And Magenta said,
    "My Nana brought them back for me,
    From far away, across the sea.
    She tangled with tigers and bit a flea
    To bring these knickers back home for me."

The girl said, "Oh, really?"

But Magenta's little brother said,
"She did not, Magenta.
She bought them at the shop."

On another proud and glorious day,
Magenta wore her spangly bangles down the street.

"Oh, my!" remarked a man,
with a parrot flapping overhead.
"Wherever did you get such
splendid and superb spangly bangles?"

And Magenta said,
   "My Nana brought them back for me,
   From far away, across the sea.
   She flipped through flowers and stung a bee
   To bring these bangles back home for me."

The man said, "Oh, really?"

But Magenta's little brother said,
"She did not, Magenta.
She bought them at the shop."

One blissful and beautiful day,
Magenta was down the street
without her tartan socks,
without her frilly knickers,
without her spangly bangles,
and . . .

without her little brother.

"Oh, my!" remarked the lady,
the girl, and the man, all together.
"Wherever is your lovely little brother?"

And Magenta said,
  "My brother is not here with me.
  He's far away, across the sea,
  Sludging through swamps and climbing a tree,
  Tangling with tigers and biting a flea,
  Flipping through flowers and stinging a bee,
  To bring a treasure back home for me."

The lady, the girl, and the man, all together, said,
"Oh, really?"

But Magenta's little brother said,
"I am not, Magenta.
I'm in the shop."

Parrot Fire Kris Northern

"Rather than zoom into the fractal you can zoom into the edge of it and continually
find the same pattern repeating itself much like the shoreline of a lake viewed from
a plane."– **Kris Northern**

Investigations

IN NUMBER, DATA, AND SPACE®

5

Power Polygons™ is a trademark of ETA/Cuisenaire®.

Use of the trademark or company name implies no relationship, sponsorship, endorsement, sale, or promotion on the part of Pearson Education, Inc., or its affiliates.

PEARSON

Glenview, Illinois • Boston, Massachusetts
Chandler, Arizona • Upper Saddle River, New Jersey

The Investigations Curriculum was developed by TERC, Cambridge, MA

T E R C

This material is based on work supported by the National Science Foundation ("NSF") under Grant No. ESI-0095450. Any opinions, findings, and conclusions or recommendations expressed in this material are those of the author(s) and do not necessarily reflect the views of the National Science Foundation.

ISBN-13: 978-0-328-60219-3

ISBN-10: 0-328-60219-1

3 4 5 6 7 8 9 10 V063 14 13 12

Co-Principal Investigators

Susan Jo Russell

Karen Economopoulos

Authors

Lucy Wittenberg
Director Grades 3–5

Karen Economopoulos
Director Grades K–2

Virginia Bastable
(SummerMath for Teachers,
Mt. Holyoke College)

Katie Hickey Bloomfield

Keith Cochran

Darrell Earnest

Arusha Hollister

Nancy Horowitz

Erin Leidl

Megan Murray

Young Oh

Beth W. Perry

Susan Jo Russell

Deborah Schifter
(Education
Development Center)

Kathy Sillman

Administrative Staff

Amy Taber
Project Manager

Beth Bergeron

Lorraine Brooks

Emi Fujiwara

Contributing Authors

Denise Baumann

Jennifer DiBrienza

Hollee Freeman

Paula Hooper

Jan Mokros

Stephen Monk
(University of Washington)

Mary Beth O'Connor

Judy Storeygard

Cornelia Tierney

Elizabeth Van Cleef

Carol Wright

Technology

Jim Hammerman

Classroom Field Work

Amy Appell

Rachel E. Davis

Traci Higgins

Julia Thompson

Collaborating Teachers

This group of dedicated teachers carried out extensive field testing in their classrooms, met regularly to discuss issues of teaching and learning mathematics, provided feedback to staff, welcomed staff into their classrooms to document students' work, and contributed both suggestions and written material that has been incorporated into the curriculum.

Bethany Altchek

Linda Amaral

Kimberly Beauregard

Barbara Bernard

Nancy Buell

Rose Christiansen

Chris Colbath-Hess

Lisette Colon

Kim Cook

Frances Cooper

Kathleen Drew

Rebeka Eston Salemi

Thomas Fisher

Michael Flynn

Holly Ghazey

Susan Gillis

Danielle Harrington

Elaine Herzog

Francine Hiller

Kirsten Lee Howard

Liliana Klass

Leslie Kramer

Melissa Lee Andrichak

Kelley Lee Sadowski

Jennifer Levitan

Mary Lou LoVecchio

Kristen McEnaney

Maura McGrail

Kathe Millett

Florence Molyneaux

Amy Monkiewicz

Elizabeth Monopoli

Carol Murray

Robyn Musser

Christine Norrman

Deborah O'Brien

Timothy O'Connor

Anne Marie O'Reilly

Mark Paige

Margaret Riddle

Karen Schweitzer

Elisabeth Seyferth

Susan Smith

Debra Sorvillo

Shoshanah Starr

Janice Szymaszek

Karen Tobin

JoAnn Trauschke

Ana Vaisenstein

Yvonne Watson

Michelle Woods

Mary Wright

Note: Unless otherwise noted, all contributors listed above were staff of the Education Research Collaborative at TERC during their work on the curriculum. Other affiliations during the time of development are listed.

Advisors

Deborah Lowenberg Ball,
University of Michigan

Hyman Bass, Professor of Mathematics and Mathematics Education
University of Michigan

Mary Canner, Principal,
Natick Public Schools

Thomas Carpenter, Professor of Curriculum and Instruction,
University of Wisconsin–Madison

Janis Freckmann, Elementary Mathematics Coordinator,
Milwaukee Public Schools

Lynne Godfrey, Mathematics Coach,
Cambridge Public Schools

Ginger Hanlon, Instructional Specialist in Mathematics,
New York City Public Schools

DeAnn Huinker, Director, Center for Mathematics and
Science Education Research, University of Wisconsin–Milwaukee

James Kaput, Professor of Mathematics,
University of Massachusetts–Dartmouth

Kate Kline, Associate Professor, Department of Mathematics
and Statistics, Western Michigan University

Jim Lewis, Professor of Mathematics,
University of Nebraska–Lincoln

William McCallum, Professor of Mathematics,
University of Arizona

Harriet Pollatsek, Professor of Mathematics,
Mt. Holyoke College

Debra Shein-Gerson, Elementary Mathematics Specialist,
Weston Public Schools

Gary Shevell, Assistant Principal,
New York City Public Schools

Liz Sweeney, Elementary Math Department,
Boston Public Schools

Lucy West, Consultant,
Metamorphosis: Teaching Learning Communities, Inc.

This revision of the curriculum was built on the work of the many authors who contributed to the first edition (published between 1994 and 1998). We acknowledge the critical contributions of these authors in developing the content and pedagogy of *Investigations:*

Authors

Joan Akers

Michael T. Battista

Douglas H. Clements

Karen Economopoulos

Marlene Kliman

Jan Mokros

Megan Murray

Ricardo Nemirovsky

Andee Rubin

Susan Jo Russell

Cornelia Tierney

Contributing Authors

Mary Berle-Carman

Rebecca B. Corwin

Rebeka Eston

Claryce Evans

Anne Goodrow

Cliff Konold

Chris Mainhart

Sue McMillen

Jerrie Moffet

Tracy Noble

Kim O'Neil

Mark Ogonowski

Julie Sarama

Amy Shulman Weinberg

Margie Singer

Virginia Woolley

Tracey Wright

PART 1

Collaborating with the Authors

Goals and Guiding Principles

Investigations in Number, Data, and Space is a K–5 mathematics curriculum designed to engage students in making sense of mathematical ideas. Six major goals guided the development of this curriculum. The curriculum is designed to

- Support students to make sense of mathematics and learn that they can be mathematical thinkers.

- Focus on computational fluency with whole numbers as a major goal of the elementary grades.

- Provide substantive work in important areas of mathematics—rational numbers, geometry, measurement, data, and early algebra—and connections among them.

- Emphasize reasoning about mathematical ideas.

- Communicate mathematics content and pedagogy to teachers.

- Engage the range of learners in understanding mathematics.

Underlying these goals are three guiding principles that are touchstones for the *Investigations* team as we approach both students and teachers as agents of their own learning:

1. *Students have mathematical ideas.* Students come to school with ideas about numbers, shapes, measurements, patterns, and data. If given the opportunity to learn in an environment that stresses making sense of mathematics, students build on the ideas they already have and learn about new mathematics they have never encountered. They learn mathematical content and develop fluency and skill that is well grounded in meaning. Students learn that they are capable of having mathematical ideas, applying what they know to new situations, and thinking and reasoning about unfamiliar problems.

2. *Teachers are engaged in ongoing learning* about mathematics content, pedagogy, and student learning. The curriculum provides material for professional development, to be used by teachers individually or in groups, that supports teachers' continued learning as they use the curriculum over several years. The *Investigations* curriculum materials are designed as much to be a dialogue with teachers as to be a core of content for students.

3. *Teachers collaborate with the students and curriculum materials* to create the curriculum as enacted in the classroom. The only way for a good curriculum to be used well is for teachers to be active participants in implementing it. Teachers use the curriculum to maintain a clear, focused, and coherent agenda for mathematics teaching. At the same time, they observe and listen carefully to students, try to understand how they are thinking, and make teaching decisions based on these observations.

The Teacher-Student-Curriculum Partnership

Mathematics teaching and learning at its best is a collaboration among teachers, students, and the curriculum. Both the teacher and the curriculum contribute to this partnership in important ways. The curriculum materials provide a coherent, carefully sequenced core of mathematics content for students and supportive professional development material for teachers. Teachers are active partners in learning the curriculum well, understanding how each mathematical focus is developed, and implementing the curriculum in a way that accommodates the needs of their particular students.

The *Investigations* curriculum was field-tested in many different classrooms, representing a range of students and teachers, over several years. Thousands of hours of classroom observation, documentation, analysis of student work, and meetings with teachers were involved. Activities and the way they are presented to students were revised again and again.

Each time a curriculum unit was tested in a classroom, no matter how many times it had been tried and revised before, there was always more to discover about how students learn and how activities can be revised and modified to support them. This process, we have come to believe, can be endless. Just as you, a classroom teacher, learn more about students' learning each year, so do those of us who develop the curriculum. At some point we decide that, considering all the evidence, the curriculum has been sufficiently tested and works well for a wide range of students.

This lengthy and detailed process has resulted in a coherent core curriculum that is based on the real needs of real students and teachers. The process has also provided ample evidence that the collaboration of the teacher is essential. Only the teacher can understand and support the particular learning needs of a particular class of students in a particular school year. Only the teacher is present every day in the classroom, observing students' work, listening to their discourse, and developing an understanding of their mathematical ideas by analyzing what they say and do. In mathematics, as in any subject, only the teacher can continually assess students' strengths and needs and think through how best to accommodate differences to involve all students in substantive and challenging work.

How *Investigations* Supports the Teacher's Role

Modifying the curriculum and making it work in your classroom requires knowing the curriculum well. It means taking the time to understand the mathematics focus of each lesson and how the mathematical ideas build over many lessons. Learning the curriculum well means holding back the urge to change activities because you think they are too easy or too difficult for your students before you have tried them and actually seen your students' work. Keep in mind that the way ideas are developed and sequenced has been

researched and tested in multiple classrooms, and many suggestions for accommodations are already built into the curriculum. Teachers tell us that they generally follow the curriculum as it is written the first year, and that they learn a great deal when activities that they thought would not work with their students turn out to be crucial to student learning.

You are an active partner in this teacher-student-curriculum partnership, and the curriculum must support your complex job by providing information about mathematics content and student learning. From the beginning, our intention in developing *Investigations* has been to create a professional development tool for teachers—a tool that provides opportunities for learning about mathematics content, how students learn, and effective pedagogy. Our design focuses as much on the teacher as learner as on the student as learner.

Two sections at the beginning of each curriculum unit, Mathematics in This Unit and Assessment in This Unit, provide an overview of the mathematics content, Math Focus Points, and benchmarks for student learning. The Math Focus Points for each session and the assessment benchmarks tell the mathematical story line of each curriculum unit so that you can productively guide students' work. Math Focus Points make explicit the purposes of the activities in each session and help you make choices about how to guide discussions. The assessment benchmarks for each curriculum unit are an aid in determining priorities and interpreting students' work.

The "teacher talk" printed in blue in each session is also an aid for focusing an activity and choosing questions to ask. It is not a script for how to address your students; it is a guide based on classroom experience with different ways of talking about mathematical ideas, introducing activities, and asking effective questions.

Teacher Notes collected at the end of each curriculum unit focus on key mathematical ideas and how students learn them. Because having students reason about, articulate, and justify their ideas is such a central part of the curriculum,

Dialogue Boxes provide examples of student discussion and teachers' efforts to focus this discussion. Additionally, examples of what students might say in class appear within the session descriptions.

To further support your work with the curriculum, this *Implementing Investigations in Grade 5* book provides an overview of the math content for the entire year (Part 3), a set of Teacher Notes that applies to the curriculum as a whole (Part 6), and a set of classroom cases written by teachers that provides examples of how they work with the range of learners in their classrooms (Part 7).

Teachers who use the *Investigations* curriculum over several years find that, as they teach a curriculum unit more than once, they gradually read more and more of the supporting material and incorporate it into their work with students. Teachers also use features such as the Teacher Notes and Dialogue Boxes as part of grade-level study groups or within other professional development structures. The better you know the curriculum and your students, the more you can internalize the mathematics focus and sequence and the better decisions you can make to support your students' learning.

Components of the Program

Curriculum Units

The curriculum at each grade level is organized into nine units (seven for kindergarten). These curriculum units are your teaching guides for the program. The unit organization is further described in the next section, "Using the Curriculum Units."

Each curriculum unit in Grade 5 offers from 3 to $4\frac{1}{2}$ weeks of work and focuses on the area of mathematics identified in the unit's subtitle.

This pacing is based on a school year that starts in early September, ends in late June, and has vacation weeks in February and April. The pacing will vary according to school calendars but may also vary depending on the needs of students, the school's years of experience with this curriculum, and other local factors.

Grade 5 Curriculum Units

Unit	Title	Number of Sessions	Suggested Pacing
1	**Number Puzzles and Multiple Towers** Multiplication and Division 1	22	September–early October
2	**Prisms and Pyramids** 3-D Geometry and Measurement	16	October
3	**Thousands of Miles, Thousands of Seats** Addition, Subtraction, and the Number System	15	November
4	**What's That Portion?** Fractions and Percents 1	21	December–January
5	**Measuring Polygons** 2-D Geometry and Measurement	18	January–February
6	**Decimals on Grids and Number Lines** Decimals, Fractions, and Percents 2	18	February–March
7	**How Many People? How Many Teams?** Multiplication and Division 2	20	March–April
8	**Growth Patterns** Patterns, Functions, and Change	13	May
9	**How Long Can You Stand on One Foot?** Data Analysis and Probability	15	June

The curriculum units are designed for use in the sequence shown. Each succeeding unit builds on the previous unit, both within and across strands. For example, the two units that focus on multiplication and division (Units 1 and 7) develop a sequence of ideas across those two units. This is also true of the two units that focus on rational numbers (Units 4 and 6). Across strands, both Unit 2 (3-D Geometry and Measurement) and Unit 8 (Patterns, Functions, and Change) use new contexts to build on the ideas of multiplication. Unit 9 (Data Analysis and Probability) also uses fractions, decimals, and percents (Units 4 and 6) to describe and analyze data and probability.

Resource Masters and Transparencies

Each Resource Masters and Transparencies CD contains the reproducible materials needed for classroom instruction. The use of all these materials for particular Investigations is specified in the curriculum units.

Investigations Software

LogoPaths Software for Grade 5 provides an environment in which students investigate movement along paths, length, perimeter, angle, and the characteristics of a variety of shapes. This software is provided as a disk to be used with Unit 5, *Measuring Polygons,* and is also available through the Pearson website.

Investigations for the Interactive Whiteboard

Each grade has whole-class instructional support that enhances the session's content as well as the daily Ten-Minute Math activity.

Differentiation and Intervention Handbook

Differentiation activities are included for each Investigation along with a quiz that can be used after an Investigation is completed.

Student Activity Book

A booklet accompanying each curriculum unit contains the consumable pages for student work, including in-class work, game recording sheets, and all pages for daily practice and for homework. The *Student Activity Book* is also available as a single volume, with all the curriculum units in one book.

Student Math Handbook

A single handbook for each grade level in Grades 1–5 offers a valuable reference to the math words and ideas introduced in the curriculum units, as well as instruction pages for playing all the games. This book is designed to be used flexibly: as a resource for students during classwork, as a book students can take home for reference while doing homework and playing math games with their families, and/or as a reference for families to better understand the work their children are doing in class.

Manipulatives Kit

A kit of materials is coordinated with the activities and games at each grade level. The Grade 5 kit includes class sets of the following items:

Connecting cubes

Color tiles

Meter/yardsticks

Rulers

Centimeter cubes

10,000 charts

Power Polygons™

Blank cubes and labels, for making number cubes

Overhead tools: transparent counters, color tiles

Cards in Card Kit

Manufactured cards are used with some of the activities and games at each grade level. The cards for Grade 5 are as follows:

Compare Cards

Digit Cards

Fraction Cards

Grade 5 Decimal Cards

Implementing *Investigations* in Grade 5

At each grade level, this guide to implementing *Investigations* includes an overview of the curriculum; suggestions for using the curriculum units in your classroom; a closer look at the mathematics content of that particular grade, including lists of the Math Focus Points for each curriculum unit; program-wide Teacher Notes that explain some key ideas underlying the curriculum; and a set of case studies about working with a range of learners that can be used for professional development.

The Curriculum Units

The curriculum unit is your main teaching tool. It is your blueprint for the sequence and purpose of the daily lessons; it also contains guidelines for assessment, suggestions for differentiating instruction, and professional development materials to support your teaching.

Structure of a Curriculum Unit

Each curriculum unit is divided into Investigations. An Investigation focuses on a set of related mathematical ideas, coordinating students' work in hands-on activities, written activities, and class discussions over a period of several days.

Investigations are divided into one-hour *sessions,* or lessons. Sessions include the following features:

- *Math Focus Points:* This list of what students will be doing mathematically highlights the goals of each session.

- *Activities:* A session contains from one to three activities, organized for work by the whole class, pairs, or individuals.

- *Discussion:* Many sessions include whole-class time during which students compare methods and results and share conclusions. A subset of the session's Focus Points helps you guide each discussion.

- *Math Workshop:* In some sessions, students work in a Math Workshop format. Individually, in pairs, or in small groups, they choose from and cycle through a set of related activities. This setup is further discussed in a later section, "All About Math Workshop" (pages 12–13).

- *Assessment:* Students are assessed through both written activities and observations; see "Assessment in This Unit" for further information.

- *Session Follow-Up:* Homework is provided for 4–5 days per week at Grade 5. In addition, each session includes a page for Daily Practice. These pages offer either ongoing review of materials from previous curriculum units or directed practice of content in the current curriculum unit. They can be used either for additional homework or for in-class practice. Relevant pages in the *Student Math Handbook* are also referenced here.

Your Math Day

The Investigations curriculum assumes that you spend 1 hour of each classroom day on mathematics, in addition to conducting brief Ten-Minute Math activities (further described later in this section and in Part 4 of this book). A chart called Today's Plan appears at the beginning of each session, laying out the suggested pacing for the activities in that 1-hour session. While you may need to adapt this structure to your particular classroom needs, be aware that it is important to move through all the activities because they are carefully designed to offer continued work on the key mathematical ideas. It is also essential that you allow time for class discussions, where students have an opportunity to articulate their own ideas, compare solutions, and consolidate understanding. See Teacher Note: Discussing Mathematical Ideas, on pages 59–61, for further information on the importance of these class discussions.

Differentiated Instruction

Within the sessions, you will regularly see a feature titled "Differentiation: Supporting the Range of Learners." This feature offers ideas for intervention or extensions related to the particular work of that session. Ideas for helping English Language Learners are offered at the beginning of the curriculum unit and where applicable in the sessions. In addition, Part 7 of this book, "Working with the Range of Learners: Classroom Cases," presents situations from actual *Investigations* classrooms and invites you to consider how these case studies can inform your own teaching practice.

Ten-Minute Math

These brief activities, described in a box below Today's Plan for each session, require 10–15 minutes of additional daily work outside of math time. These activities, an important part of the *Investigations* curriculum, offer ongoing skill building, practice, and review that supports the regular math work; they also reinforce the work students have done in previous units; and helps students increase their repertoire of strategies for mental calculation and problem solving. Part 4 of this book, "Ten-Minute Math," provides detailed explanations of the activities to plan for Grade 5.

Assessment in This Unit

Opportunities for assessment are carefully woven throughout the curriculum units. A section at the beginning of each curriculum unit identifies the benchmarks students will be expected to meet and specifies key activities you can observe, as well as the particular assessment activities where students will produce written work for your review. The final session in each curriculum unit is devoted to the End-of-Unit Assessment. Each written assessment in the curriculum unit is accompanied by a Teacher Note that provides examples of student work and guidelines that help you assess whether your students are meeting the benchmarks. For observed assessments, an assessment checklist is provided; here you can record notes about what students understand as you observe them engaged in the session's activities.

▲ **An example of an Assessment Checklist**

"Ongoing Assessment: Observing Students at Work" is a regular feature of the sessions. It identifies the particular math focus and lists questions for you to consider as you observe your students solving problems, playing math games, and working on activities. Teacher observations are an important part of ongoing assessment. Although individual observations may be little more than snapshots of a student's experience with a single activity, when considered together over time, they can provide an informative and detailed picture. These observations can be useful in documenting and assessing a student's growth and offer important sources of information when preparing for family conferences or writing student reports.

You may want to develop a system to record and keep track of your observations of students. The most important aspect of a record-keeping system is that it be both manageable and useful for you. Some teachers use systems such as the following:

- Jot down observations of students' work on a class list of names. Because the space is somewhat limited, it is not possible to write lengthy notes; however, when kept over time, these short observations provide important information.

- Place stick-on address labels on a clipboard. Take notes on individual students and then peel these labels off and put them in a file for each student.

- Jot down brief notes at the end of each week. Some teachers find that this is a useful way of reflecting on the class as a whole, on the curriculum, and on individual students. Planning for the next week's activities can benefit from these weekly reflections.

Observation checklists, student work on written assessments, and other examples of students' written work can be collected in a portfolio. Suggestions for particular work that might be saved in a portfolio are listed at the beginning of each curriculum unit, under "Assessment in This Unit."

Professional Development

One guiding principle of the *Investigations* curriculum is to provide support that helps teachers improve their own understanding of the mathematics that they are teaching and the learning that they observe in their students. To this end, the following materials are included in the curriculum for teachers' professional development:

- *Mathematics in This Unit:* An essay at the beginning of each curriculum unit explains in detail the Mathematical Emphases of the unit, the Math Focus Points related to each area of emphasis, and the work students will be doing in each area.

- *Algebra Connections in This Unit:* This essay, appearing in each of the number and operations units and in the patterns, functions, and change units, explains how the activities and ideas of the unit are laying a foundation for students' later work with algebra.

- *Math Notes, Teaching Notes, and Algebra Notes:* Found in the margins of the sessions, these brief notes provide information about mathematics content or student thinking, as well as teaching tips to help teachers better understand the work of that session.

- *Teacher Notes:* These essays, collected at the end of each curriculum unit, provide further practical information about the mathematics content and how students learn it. Many of the notes were written in response to questions from teachers or to discuss important issues that arose in field-test classrooms. They offer teachers help with thinking about mathematical ideas that may be unfamiliar to them; they also provide guidance for observing and assessing students' work.

- *Dialogue Boxes:* Also at the end of each curriculum unit are Dialogue Boxes that reflect classroom scenarios related to the activities of the unit. Since these Dialogue Boxes are based on actual teacher-student interactions, you learn how students typically express their mathematical ideas, what issues and confusions arise in their thinking, and how some teachers have chosen to guide particular class discussions.

Working with Families

Families are important partners with schools in the process of teaching mathematics. Because the teaching of mathematics has been evolving, many families may be unfamiliar with the approaches taken by the *Investigations* curriculum. For this reason, a number of Family Letters are provided. In Grade 5, these letters include the following:

- The first Family Letter in each curriculum unit, About the Mathematics in This Unit, introduces families to the mathematics that their children will be doing and to the benchmarks for that unit.

- A second letter in each curriculum unit, Related Activities to Try at Home, is sent home a few days after the first. It suggests related activities that families can do together and story or picture books that support students' work in mathematics.

- An additional letter provided in the first curriculum unit of the year, About Mathematics Homework, gives suggestions for helping students with their homework by establishing a regular time for homework, setting up a good working environment, and asking productive questions.

- Particular to Grade 5, one more Family Letter focuses on ways students who are not fluent with the multiplication combinations (facts) can practice them and how parents can support this work at home. The letter on Practicing Multiplication Combinations is provided with Unit 1, *Number Puzzles and Multiple Towers.*

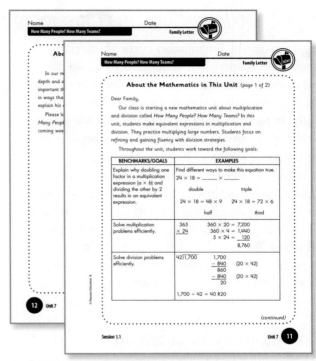

▲ **An example of a Family Letter**

The *Student Math Handbook* is another valuable tool for working with families. The Math Words and Ideas section of this book provides an overview of the year's mathematics work, a closer look at the ideas and the kinds of problems students encounter, examples of student solutions, and questions that families and students can talk about together. The handbook also describes some of the games that students will use within the curriculum units and how these games can be incorporated into home use.

Setting Up the *Investigations* Classroom

As you begin using the *Investigations* curriculum, you may find yourself making decisions about how to set up the tables and chairs in your classroom and where to keep your materials. Students will at various times need to work individually, in pairs or small groups, and as a whole class. When working in pairs or small groups, they need to be able to see one another's work and listen to one another's ideas. Bringing students together for whole-group discussion is also a regular feature of the curriculum, and during these discussions it is important that students can easily see and hear one another. Ways of making this work are further discussed in the Teacher Note: Discussing Mathematical Ideas, on pages 59–61. You must also find ways to make materials and games easily accessible and consider how to organize the room for Math Workshops.

Materials as Tools for Learning

In an active mathematics classroom, certain basic materials should be available at all times: connecting cubes, pencils, blank paper, grid paper, calculators, things to count with, and measuring tools. Some activities in the curriculum require glue sticks and scissors or tape. Stick-on notes and large paper for posters are also useful materials.

So students can independently get what they need at any time, they should know where these materials are kept, how they are stored, and how they need to be returned to the storage area. For example, connecting cubes are best stored in towers of 10 and should be replaced in these towers when an activity is completed.

Rationale

Tools and materials are used throughout the *Investigations* curriculum. Students of all ages benefit from being able to use materials to model problems and explain their thinking.

It is important to encourage all students to use tools and materials, such as connecting cubes, Power Polygons, and measuring tools. If materials are used only when someone is having difficulty, students may get the mistaken idea that using materials is a less sophisticated and less valued way of solving a problem. Encourage students to talk about how they used certain materials. They should see how different people, including the teacher, use a variety of materials in solving the same problem.

The more available materials are, the more likely students are to use them. Having materials available means that they are readily accessible to students and that students are allowed to make decisions about which tools to use and when to use them. In much the same way as you choose the best tool to use for certain projects or tasks, students should be encouraged to think about which material best meets their needs.

Using concrete materials in the classroom may be a new experience for many students and teachers. Before introducing new materials, think about how you want students to use and care for them, including how they will be stored.

Introducing a New Material

Students need time to explore a new material before using it in structured activities. By freely exploring with new materials, students will discover many of the important characteristics of the new material and will gain some understanding of where it might make sense to use it. Although some free exploration should be done during regular math time, many teachers make materials such as Power Polygons available to students during free time or before or after school.

Plan for how materials will be cleaned up at the end of each class. Most teachers find that stopping 5 minutes before the end of class gives students time to clean up materials, organize and turn in their work, and double-check the floor for any stray materials.

Storing Materials

Store materials where they are easily accessible to students. Many teachers store materials in plastic tubs or shoe boxes arranged on a bookshelf or along a windowsill. In addition to Power Polygons, color tiles, and connecting cubes, items such as calculators and paper (blank and grid) are important mathematical tools that should be available to students.

Games in the *Investigations* Curriculum

The games included in this curriculum are a central part of the mathematics in each curriculum unit, not just an enrichment activity. Games are used to develop concepts and to practice skills, such as learning to sort and classify polygons, estimating products, or adding fractions and decimals. The rationale for using games is as follows:

- Games provide engaging opportunities for students to deepen their understanding of the number system and operations and to practice computation.

- Playing games encourages strategic mathematical thinking as students find an optimal way (rather than just any way) of "winning" the game.

- Games provide repeated practice without requiring the teacher to provide new problems.

- While students are playing the games, the teacher is free to observe students or to work with individuals or small groups.

Before introducing a game to students, it is important that you play the game for yourself to learn the mathematical ideas that students encounter as they play the game. For some games, variations are offered. Before using these variations, or any others you might think of, consider how changing the rules of the game changes the mathematical ideas with which students are working.

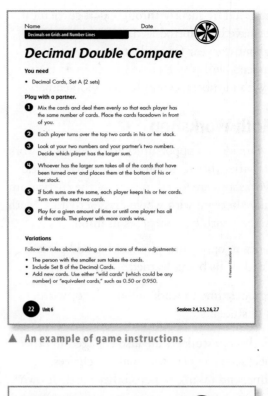

▲ An example of game instructions

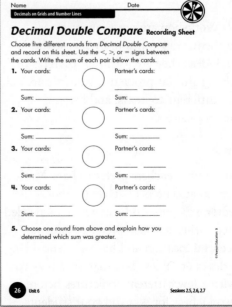

▲ An example of a game recording sheet

Games are often played frequently throughout a curriculum unit. Once games have been introduced, consider leaving them out throughout the year for students to play. It is expected that students will play a game many times as they develop fluency with numbers, computation, and geometry.

All About Math Workshop

Math Workshop provides an opportunity for students to work on a variety of activities that focus on similar mathematical content. Math Workshops are found in most of the curriculum units and generally alternate with whole-class activities. Math Workshop is designed with two purposes in mind:

1. To give students an opportunity to develop and practice the concepts and skills being learned

2. To give the teacher time to work one-on-one or with small groups of students

During Math Workshop, students are also engaged in other key aspects of their school experience: making choices, planning their time, and taking responsibility for their own learning.

The activities in Math Workshop are not sequential; as students move among them, they continually revisit the important concepts and ideas they are learning. By repeatedly playing a game, or solving similar problems, students are able to refine strategies, use different contexts, and bring new knowledge to familiar experiences.

Setting Up Math Workshop

Organizing Materials Some teachers prefer to have Math Workshop activities set up at centers or stations around the classroom. At each center, students find the materials needed to complete the activity. Other teachers prefer to have materials stored in a central location and have students bring the materials to their desks or tables. You may find that you need to experiment with a few different structures before finding a setup that works best for you and your students.

Materials should be readily accessible to students, and students should be expected to take responsibility for cleaning up and returning materials to their appropriate storage locations. Giving students a "5 minutes until cleanup" warning before the end of an activity session allows them to finish what they are working on and prepare for the upcoming transition, which is often to a class discussion.

Organizing the Students Each Math Workshop generally includes three to five activities that students do over several class sessions. Support students in organizing their time to complete the activities. Initially you may need to help students plan what they do and in what order, but as the year goes on, students should learn to make their choices, get their materials, engage with an activity for enough time to benefit from it, and then switch activities, without your help.

Often when a new activity is introduced, many students want to do it first. Assure them that they will be able to work on each activity. Some students may want to return to the same activity over and over again, such as a game, without trying other activities. Make sure these students do a different activity first, and then choose the favorite activity as a second choice. Other students may need to be encouraged to use their time efficiently to complete all activities. You may want to limit the number of students who work on a Math Workshop activity at one time. In some cases, the quantity of materials available limits the number of students who can do an activity at any one time. In others, limiting the number of students at one activity gives them the opportunity to work in smaller groups and requires students to make choices among activities.

We do not recommend that you organize students into groups and have each group at each activity for a set amount of time. While this method ensures that each student engages in each activity, it does not provide the flexibility and differentiation needed in the classroom. One student may have accomplished a task and need to move to a different activity, while another may be engaged in good mathematical work at a particular activity for a longer time. For the same reason, we also do not recommend that you conduct Math Workshop activities as whole class activities, one after the other.

The Role of the Student

Establish clear guidelines when you introduce Math Workshop activities. Discuss students' responsibilities:

- Work on every activity at least once.

- Be productively engaged during Math Workshop.

- Ask questions of other students when you don't understand or feel stuck. (Some teachers establish the rule, "Ask two other students before me," which requires students to check with two peers before coming to the teacher for help.)

Students should also determine a method to keep track of their work. Some teachers list the choices for sessions on a chart, the board, or an overhead projector to help students keep track of what they need to do. As students finish an activity, they write it on a list and place any work they have done in their folders.

The Role of the Teacher

Establishing the Routine You will probably find that much of your time during the initial Math Workshops is spent circulating around the classroom helping students get settled into activities and monitoring the overall management of the classroom. Once routines are familiar and well established, students will become more independent and responsible for their work during Math Workshop. This will allow you to spend more concentrated periods of time observing the class as a whole or working with individuals and small groups.

Making Expectations Explicit The amount of work that students are expected to complete will vary from classroom to classroom. Some activities include extensions and additional problems for students who need further practice or extra challenge. Suggestions are also made in the Math Workshop activities and the "Supporting the Range of Learners" sections in the Math Workshop sessions. As students begin each Math Workshop, make certain students know which activities they are expected to complete.

Individual and Small Group Work Math Workshop allows teachers to observe and listen to students while they work. At times, you may want to meet with individual students, pairs, or small groups who might need help (or additional challenges). You may also want to focus on particular students in order to get a better sense of their math understanding. Recording your observations of students will help you keep track of how they are interacting with materials and solving problems.

Sometimes one of the Math Workshop activities is a formal observed assessment. This type of assessment provides an opportunity to assess students as they work on a set of problems or play a game. You can record your observations on the assessment checklist that is provided in the Resources Binder.

Number and Operations: Whole Numbers

In Grade 5, students practice the strategies they know for the addition, subtraction, multiplication, and division of whole numbers to improve their fluency and apply these strategies to solving problems with large numbers. Students continue to expand their understanding of the meaning of these operations by articulating, representing, and justifying generalizations about numbers and operations. They expand their knowledge of the structure of place value and the base-ten number system as they work with numbers in the hundred thousands and beyond.

Multiplication and Division

Students consolidate their understanding of the computational strategies they use for multiplication. All students should be able to carry out strategies that involve breaking one or both factors apart, multiplying each part of one factor by each part of the other factor, then combining the partial products. They also practice notating their solutions clearly. They use representations and story contexts to connect these strategies, which are based on the distributive property of multiplication, to the meaning of multiplication. As part of their study of multiplication, students analyze and compare multiplication algorithms, including the U.S. algorithm for multiplication.

Examples of Multiplication Strategies

Breaking numbers apart by addition:

$$148 \times 42 =$$

$$40 \times 100 = 4{,}000$$

$$40 \times 40 = 1{,}600$$

$$40 \times 8 = 320$$

$$2 \times 100 = 200$$

$$2 \times 40 = 80$$

$$2 \times 8 = 16$$

$$4{,}000 + 1{,}600 + 320 + 200 + 80 + 16 = 6{,}216$$

$$148 \times 42 =$$

$$100 \times 42 = 4{,}200$$

$$48 \times 40 = 1{,}920$$

$$48 \times 2 = 96$$

$$4{,}200 + 1{,}920 + 96 = 6{,}216$$

Changing one number to create an easier problem:

$$148 \times 42 =$$

$$150 \times 42 = 6{,}300 \ (100 \times 42 + \tfrac{1}{2} \text{ of } 100 \times 42)$$

$$2 \times 42 = 84$$

$$6{,}300 - 84 = 6{,}216$$

Students continue to learn ways to solve division problems fluently, focusing on the relationship between multiplication and division. They solve division problems by relating them to missing factor problems (e.g., $462 \div 21 = \underline{\hspace{1cm}}$ and $\underline{\hspace{1cm}} \times 21 = 462$), by building up groups of the divisor, and by using multiples of 10 to solve problems more efficiently. As students refine their computation strategies for division, they find ways to use what they already know and understand well (familiar factor pairs, multiples of 10, relationships between numbers, etc.) to break apart the harder problems into easier problems. They also work on notating their solutions clearly and concisely.

___ × 21 = 1,275 6 × 21 = 126 60 × 21 = 1,260 1,275 − 1,260 = 15 Answer: 60 R15	1,275 ÷ 21 = 630 ÷ 21 = 30 1,275 − 630 = 645 630 ÷ 21 = 30 645 − 630 = 15 1,260 ÷ 21 = 60 Answer: 60 R15
21)1,275 10 × 21 = 210 20 × 21 = 420 30 × 21 = 630 60 × 21 = 1,260 60 R15 21)1,275	21)1,275 − 420 20 × 21 = 420 855 − 630 30 × 21 = 630 225 − 210 10 × 21 = 210 15 20 + 30 + 10 = 60 Answer: 60 R15

Examples of clear and concise notation

Students also study the underlying properties of numbers and operations and make and justify general claims based on these properties. They study the relationship between a number and its factors, which supports mental computation strategies for multiplication and division with whole numbers. For example, students consider multiplication expressions related by place value (e.g., $3 \times 6 = 18$; $3 \times 60 = 3 \times 6 \times 10 = 180$) and equivalent multiplication expressions (e.g., $24 \times 18 = 12 \times 36$ or $24 \times 18 = 72 \times 6$). This work includes finding longer and longer multiplication expressions for a number and considering the prime factorization of a number.

Students also investigate equivalent expressions in multiplication and division. For example, they investigate why doubling one factor and halving the other factor (or tripling and thirding, etc.) in a multiplication expression of the form $a \times b$ maintains the same product. They also examine how and why the ratio between the dividend and the divisor must be maintained to generate equivalent division expressions. In this work, students develop mathematical arguments based on representations of the operations.

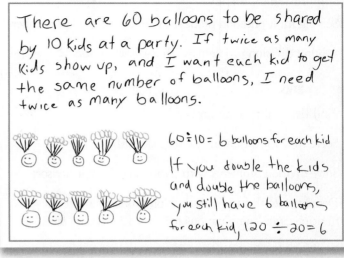

Sample Student Work

Mathematical Emphases

Whole-Number Operations

- Reasoning about numbers and their factors

- Understanding and using the relationship between multiplication and division to solve division problems

- Representing the meaning of multiplication and division

- Reasoning about equivalent expressions in multiplication and division

Computational Fluency

- Solving multiplication problems with 2- and 3-digit numbers
- Solving division problems with 2-digit divisors

Benchmarks

- Find the factors of a number.
- Solve multiplication problems efficiently.
- Solve division problems with 1-digit and 2-digit divisors.
- Demonstrate fluency with division problems related to the multiplication combinations to 12×12 (division facts).
- Explain why doubling one factor in a multiplication expression ($a \times b$) and dividing the other by two results in an equivalent expression.
- Solve division problems efficiently.

Addition, Subtraction, and the Number System

In Grade 5, students extend their knowledge of the base-ten number system, working with numbers in the hundred thousands and beyond. In their place-value work, students focus on adding and subtracting multiples of 100 and 1,000 to multidigit numbers and explaining the results. This work helps them develop reasonable estimates for sums and differences when solving problems with large numbers. Students apply their understanding of addition to multistep problems with large numbers. They develop increased fluency as they study a range of strategies and generalize the strategies they understand to solve problems with large numbers.

$90,945 - 1,000 =$

$90,945 - 1,200 =$

$90,945 - 1,210 =$

$90,945 - 1,310 =$

Students practice and refine their strategies for solving subtraction problems. They also classify and analyze the logic of different strategies; they then learn more about the operation of subtraction by thinking about how these strategies work. Students consider which subtraction problems can be solved easily by changing one of the numbers and then adjusting the difference. As they discuss and analyze this approach, they visualize important properties of subtraction. By revisiting the steps and notation of the U.S. algorithm for subtraction, and comparing it to other algorithms, students analyze how regrouping enables subtracting by place, with results that are all in positive numbers.

Examples of Subtraction Strategies

Subtracting in parts

$3,451 - 1,287 =$

$3,451 - 1,200 = 2,251$

$2,251 - 80 = 2,171$

$2,171 - 7 = 2,164$

Adding up	Subtracting back
$3,451 - 1,287 =$	$3,451 - 1,287 =$
$1,287 + 13 = 1,300$	$3,451 - 51 = 3,400$
$1,300 + 2,100 = 3,400$	$3,400 - 2,100 = 1,300$
$3,400 + 251 = 3,451$	$1,300 - 13 = 1,287$
$13 + 2,100 + 51 = 2,164$	$51 + 2,100 + 13 = 2,164$

Changing the numbers

$3,451 - 1,287 =$

$3,451 - 1,300 = 2,151$

$2,151 + 13 = 2,164$

$3,451 - 1,287 =$

(add 13 to both numbers to create an equivalent problem)

$3,451 - 1,287 = 3,464 - 1,300$
$= 2,164$

Mathematical Emphases

The Base-Ten Number System

• Extending knowledge of the number system to 100,000 and beyond

Whole-Number Operations

• Examining and using strategies for subtracting whole numbers

Computational Fluency

• Adding and subtracting accurately and efficiently

Benchmarks

• Read, write, and sequence numbers to 100,000.

• Solve subtraction problems accurately and efficiently, choosing from a variety of strategies.

Rational Numbers

The major focus of the work with rational numbers in Grade 5 is on understanding relationships among fractions, decimals, and percents. Students make comparisons and identify equivalent fractions, decimals, and percents, and they develop strategies for adding and subtracting fractions and decimals.

In a study of fractions and percents, students work with halves, thirds, fourths, fifths, sixths, eighths, tenths, and twelfths. They develop strategies for finding percent equivalents for these fractions so that they are able to easily move back and forth between fractions and percents and choose what is most helpful in solving a particular problem, such as finding percentages or fractions of a group.

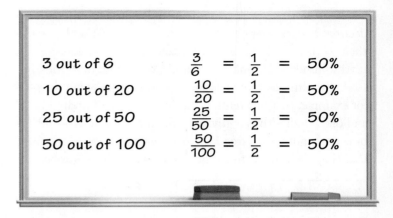

Students use their knowledge of fraction equivalents, fraction-percent equivalents, the relationship of fractions to landmarks such as $\frac{1}{2}$, 1, and 2, and other relationships to decide which of two fractions is greater. They carry out addition and subtraction of fractional amounts in ways that make sense to them by using representations such as rectangles, rotation on a clock, and the number line to visualize and reason about fraction equivalents and relationships.

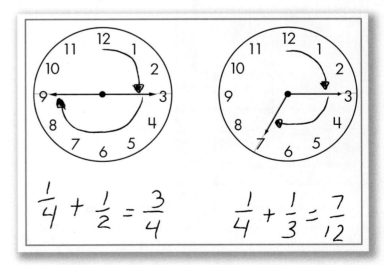

Students continue to develop their understanding of how decimal fractions represent quantities less than 1 and extend their work with decimals to thousandths. By representing tenths, hundredths, and thousandths on rectangular grids, students learn about the relationships among these numbers—for example, that one tenth is equivalent to ten hundredths and one hundredth is equivalent to ten thousandths—and how these numbers extend the place-value structure of tens that they understand from their work with whole numbers.

$$\begin{array}{ll} 0.625 & 0.8 \\ + \, 0.75 & 0.75 \\ \hline 1.375 & + \, 0.625 \\ + \, 0.8 & \hline 2.175 \\ \hline 2.175 & \end{array}$$

$0.8 + 0.75 + 0.625$

$2.1 + 0.07 + 0.005 =$
2.175

$0.625 + 0.8 = 1.425$
$(1.425 + 0.75)$
$1.425 + 0.7 = 2.125$
$2.125 + 0.05 = 2.175$

Students extend their knowledge of fraction-decimal equivalents by studying how fractions represent division and carrying out that division to find an equivalent decimal. They compare, order, and add decimal fractions (tenths, hundredths, and thousandths) by carefully identifying the place value of the digits in each number and using representations to visualize the quantities represented by these numbers.

Mathematical Emphases
Rational Numbers
- Understanding the meaning of fractions and percents
- Comparing fractions
- Understanding the meaning of decimal fractions
- Comparing decimal fractions

Computation with Rational Numbers
- Adding and subtracting fractions
- Adding decimals

Benchmarks
- Use fraction-percent equivalents to solve problems about the percentage of a quantity.
- Order fractions with like and unlike denominators.
- Add fractions through reasoning about fraction equivalents and relationships.
- Read, write, and interpret decimal fractions to thousandths.
- Order decimals to the thousandths.
- Add decimal fractions through reasoning about place value, equivalents, and representations.

Patterns, Functions, and Change

In Grade 5, students continue their work from Grades 3 and 4 by examining, representing, and describing situations in which the rate of change is constant. Students create tables and graphs to represent the relationship between two variables in a variety of contexts. They also articulate general rules for each situation. For example, consider the perimeters of the following set of rectangles made from rows of tiles with three tiles in each row:

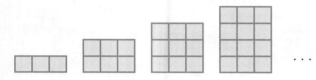

If the value of one variable (the number of rows of three tiles) is known, the corresponding value of the other variable (the perimeter of the rectangle) can be calculated. Students express these rules in words and then in symbolic notation. For example:

> To find the perimeter of a 3-across rectangle, multiply the number of rows by 2 and add 6.
>
> $p = (2 \times n) + 6$ (where p is the value of the perimeter and n is the number of rows)

For the first time in Grade 5, students create graphs for situations in which the rate of change is itself changing—for example, the change in the area of a square as a side increases by a constant increment—and consider why the shape of the graph is not a straight line as it is for situations with a constant rate of change.

Throughout their work, students move among tables, graphs, and equations and between those representations and the situation they represent. Their work with symbolic notation is closely connected to the context with which they are working. By moving back and forth between the contexts, their own ways of describing general rules in words, and symbolic notation, students learn how this notation can carry mathematical meaning.

Mathematical Emphases

Using Tables and Graphs

- Using tables to represent change

- Using graphs to represent change

Linear Change

- Describing and representing situations with a constant rate of change

Nonlinear Change

- Describing and representing situations in which the rate of change is not constant

Benchmarks

- Create tables and graphs to represent the relationship between two variables.

- Use tables and graphs to compare two situations with constant rates of change.

- Use symbolic notation to represent the value of one variable in terms of another variable in situations with constant rates of change.

Data Analysis and Probability

Students continue to develop their understanding of data analysis in Grade 5 by collecting, representing, describing, and interpreting numerical data. Students' work in this unit focuses on comparing two sets of data collected from experiments. Students develop a question to compare two groups, objects, or conditions. (Sample questions: Which toy car goes farther after rolling down the ramp? Which paper bridge holds more weight?) They consider how to ensure a consistent procedure for their experiment and discuss the importance of multiple trials. Using representations of data, including line plots and bar graphs, students describe the shape of the data—where the data are concentrated and how they are spread across the range. They summarize the data for each group, object, or condition and use these summaries, including medians, to back up their conclusions and arguments. By carrying out a complete data investigation, from formulating a question through drawing conclusions from their data, students gain an understanding of data analysis as a tool for learning about the world.

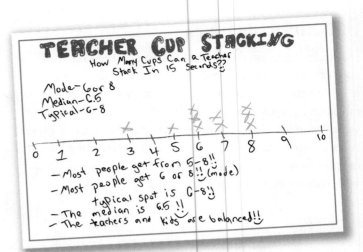

Sample Student Work

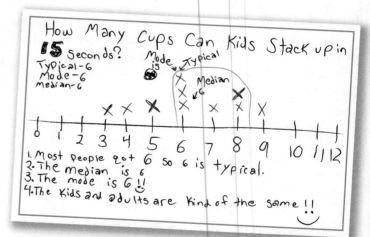

Sample Student Work

In their work with probability, students describe and predict the likelihood of events and compare theoretical probabilities with actual outcomes of many trials. They use fractions to express the probabilities of the possible outcomes (e.g., landing on the green part of the spinner, landing on the white part of the spinner). Then they conduct experiments to see what actually occurs. The experiments lead to questions about theoretical and experimental probability; for example, if half the area of a spinner is colored green and half is colored white, why doesn't the spinner land on green exactly half the time?

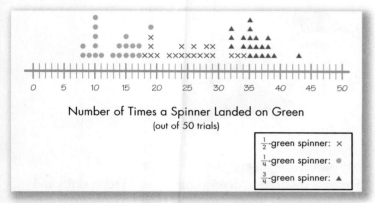

Number of Times a Spinner Landed on Green
(out of 50 trials)

$\frac{1}{2}$-green spinner: ×
$\frac{1}{4}$-green spinner: ●
$\frac{3}{4}$-green spinner: ▲

Line plot from Comparing Spinner Results discussion in Unit 9, How Long Can You Stand on One Foot?

Mathematical Emphases

Data Analysis

- Representing data

- Describing, summarizing, and comparing data

- Analyzing and interpreting data

- Designing and carrying out a data investigation

Probability

- Describing the probability of an event

Benchmarks

- Describe major features of a set of data represented in a line plot or bar graph, and quantify the description by using the median or fractional parts of the data.

- Draw conclusions about how two groups compare based on summarizing the data for each group.

- Design and carry out an experiment in order to compare two groups.

- Use a decimal, fraction, or percent to describe and compare the theoretical probabilities of events with a certain number of equally likely outcomes.

Geometry and Measurement

In their work with geometry and measurement in Grade 5, students further develop their understanding of the attributes of two-dimensional (2-D) shapes, find the measure of angles of polygons, determine the volume of three-dimensional (3-D) shapes, and work with area and perimeter. Students examine the characteristics of polygons, including a variety of triangles, quadrilaterals, and regular polygons. They consider various questions about the classification of geometric figures, for example:

Are all squares rectangles?

Are all rectangles parallelograms?

If all squares are rhombuses, then are all rhombuses squares?

---

1. Samantha says this figure is called a rhombus. Felix says it is called a square. Joshua says it is called a parallelogram.

Can they all be right? How is that possible? Explain.

Question 1 from Resource Masters, M17 in Unit 5, Measuring Polygons

They investigate angle sizes in a set of polygons and measure angles of 30, 45, 60, 90, 120, and 150 degrees by comparing the angles of these shapes. Students also investigate perimeter and area. They consider how changes to the shape of a rectangle can affect one of the measures and not the other (e.g., two shapes that have the same area don't necessarily have the same perimeter) and examine the relationship between area and perimeter in similar figures.

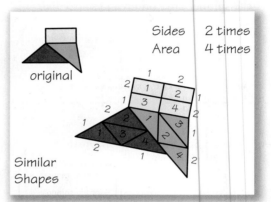

Students continue to develop their visualization skills and their understanding of the relationship between 2-D pictures and the 3-D objects they represent. Students determine the volume of boxes (rectangular prisms) made from 2-D patterns and create patterns for boxes to hold a certain number of cubes. They develop strategies for determining the number of cubes in 3-D arrays by mentally organizing the cubes—for example, as a stack of three rectangular layers, each three by four cubes. Students deepen their understanding of the relationship between volume and the linear dimensions of length, width, and height. Once students have developed viable strategies for finding the volume of rectangular prisms, they extend their understanding of volume to other solids, such as pyramids, cylinders, and cones, measured in cubic units.

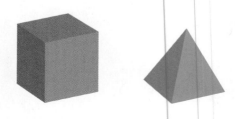

Mathematical Emphases

Features of Shape

- Describing and classifying 2-D figures

- Describing and measuring angles

- Creating and describing similar shapes

- Translating between 2-D and 3-D shapes

Linear and Area Measurement

- Finding the perimeter and area of rectangles

Volume

- Structuring rectangular prisms and determining their volume

- Structuring prisms, pyramids, cylinders, and cones and determining their volume

Benchmarks

- Identify different quadrilaterals by their attributes and know that some quadrilaterals can be classified in more than one way.

- Use known angle sizes to determine the sizes of other angles. (30, 45, 60, 90, 120, and 150 degrees)

- Determine the perimeter and area of rectangles.

- Identify mathematically similar polygons.

- Find the volume of rectangular prisms.

- Use standard units to measure volume.

- Identify how the dimensions of a box change when the volume is changed.

- Explain the relationship between the volumes of prisms and pyramids with the same base and height.

Curriculum Unit	1	2	3	4	5	6	7	8	9
Ten-Minute Math									
Estimation and Number Sense		•	•	•		•	•	•	•
Guess My Rule				•					
Number Puzzles	•						•		
Practicing Place Value			•			•		•	
Quick Images	•	•			•				
Quick Survey					•				•

Preview

Ten-Minute Math activities appear throughout Grades 3–5. These short activities, designed to take no longer than 10 minutes, support and balance the in-depth work of each curriculum unit. After their first introduction in a math session, they are intended for use outside of math time. Some teachers use them to bring the whole class together just before or after lunch or recess or at the beginning or end of the day.

At Grade 5, six Ten-Minute Math activities are woven through the nine curriculum units. The following pages contain complete procedures for these activities, including the variations intended for use in Grade 5. Specific suggestions for use are found in Today's Plan for each session. It is recommended that you begin with the suggested daily problems and adapt them to fit the needs of your students throughout the year. Any needed preparation is noted in the Investigation Planner.

Estimation and Number Sense

Students make the closest estimate they can, within 30 seconds, for a problem that is created using Digit Cards and a given template (such as __ __ __ × __ __). Students explain and discuss their strategies for making good estimates. This activity provides practice with estimation and mental computation with all four operations of whole numbers.

Math Focus Points

Students use their knowledge of landmarks and numerical reasoning to estimate the solution to a given computation problem.

◆ Estimating solutions to 2-digit to 4-digit multiplication and division problems

◆ Estimating solutions to addition and subtraction problems with fractions and mixed numbers

◆ Breaking apart, reordering, or changing numbers mentally to determine a reasonable estimate

Estimation and Number Sense is introduced in Session 1.4 in Unit 2, *Prisms and Pyramids;* it also appears in Unit 4, *What's That Portion?* in Unit 6, *Decimals on Grids and Number Lines;* and in Unit 8, *Growth Patterns.*

Materials

- Digit Cards

- Overhead projector and transparencies (optional)

Basic Activity

Step 1 **Display the problem template.** Templates may involve any operation and any reasonable number of digits. Here are some examples:

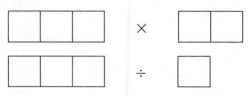

Step 2 **Place digits to establish the problem without disclosing it.** The leader draws one Digit Card for each slot in the template and records the digits, in the order drawn, without showing anyone. In this example, the cards drawn are 7, 4, 1, 0, 3. The template looks like this:

Note that because of the random way Digit Cards are drawn, 0 will sometimes turn up as the leftmost digit in a number, as in this example (03). Students need to understand that 03 is the same as 3. However, if a problem that requires dividing by 0 (such as 491 ÷ 0) is created, the leader should draw a new card to replace the 0.

When using a subtraction template, always consider making the first number in the template (the minuend) one place larger than the second number (the subtrahend), for example, a 4-digit number minus a 3-digit number. Alternatively, deal three digits for each number and create a problem where the minuend is larger. For example, the first three cards dealt are 4, 0, 8, and the last three cards dealt are 5, 7, and 1. Create the problem 804 − 571.

Step 3 **Reveal the problem. Students work for 30 seconds to estimate the answer.** Students should solve as much of the problem as they can mentally. Students may write down partial solutions. Depending on the problem, expect that some students will find the exact answer. For example, to solve 741 × 03, a student first makes a quick estimate—2,100 (700 × 3) or 2,250 (750 × 3)—and then solves much of the problem mentally during the time remaining. Students might write 2,100, 120, and 3 on their papers or add the partial products mentally to find the answer: 2,223.

Step 4 **Students explain their solutions.** Ask two or three students to explain how they came up with their estimate and record these steps on the board. Ask questions such as the following:

What part(s) of the problem did you solve to make your estimate? How much of the problem still needs to be solved?

Do you think your estimate is smaller or larger than the actual answer? Why?

Variations

Exact Answers

Follow the procedure in the basic activity but ask students to calculate the exact answer after they have estimated the answer. Students then compare their estimates with the actual answer and find the difference. As students gain experience with estimation, they work toward finding a smaller and smaller difference between their estimate and the actual answer.

Closest Estimate

Closest Estimate is introduced in Session 1.4 in Unit 3, *Thousands of Miles, Thousands of Seats;* it also appears in Unit 7, *How Many People? How Many Teams?* and in Unit 9, *How Long Can You Stand on One Foot?*

Materials

- Overhead projector or chart paper

- Transparencies T36–T38, T71–T76, T85–T88, *Closest Estimate*

Name			Date	
How Many People? How Many Teams?				

Estimation and Number Sense: Closest Estimate (page 4 of 6)

19. 417 × 38 ≈	1,600	12,000	16,000
20. 292 × 62 ≈	1,800	12,000	18,000
21. 372 × 49 ≈	18,000	20,000	22,000
22. 511 ÷ 4 ≈	75	100	125
23. 60 × 27 ≈	1,200	1,600	2,000
24. 605 × 32 ≈	1,800	18,000	180,000

Sessions 3.7, 4.3   Unit 7 M9

▲ **Resource Masters, Unit 7 M9; Transparencies, T74**

Step 1 Present the problem. Show students each problem one at a time along with the three possible estimates. Give them about 30 seconds to consider which estimate is closest to the actual answer.

Step 2 Discuss strategies. Collect a few responses and discuss any disagreements. Students should defend their choice of answers by explaining how they made their estimates. Ask questions like the following:

How did you change the numbers to make the problem easier?

Why do you think that this estimate is closer than this one?

Is this estimate more or less than the actual answer? How do you know?

Guess My Rule

In this classification game, students decide, through careful observation, questioning, and logical reasoning, what characteristics a group of people have in common. The leader secretly establishes a rule, using attributes such as "HAS BROWN HAIR" (describing a portion of the class). The leader then identifies the fractional part of the group that follows the rule. Students use the evidence to form hypotheses and then systematically make guesses to deduce the rule.

Math Focus Points

Students use evidence that includes a given fractional part of a group to identify common characteristics of the group.

◆ Identifying fractions of a group

◆ Using evidence and formulating questions to make hypotheses about the common characteristics in a group

◆ Systematically eliminating possibilities

Guess My Rule is introduced in Session 1.2 in Unit 4, *What's That Portion?* and appears in this unit only.

Basic Activity

Step 1 Choose a rule and identify the fraction. People might be classified by their gender or hair color, what they are wearing on a given day, and so on. Choose a group of students and a visually obvious rule that describes a fraction of those students, such as "HAS BROWN HAIR," "WEARING RED," or "WEARING A WATCH." Tell students that you are thinking of a rule that fits one half (or whatever the fraction is) of the group.

Step 2 Students work to discover the rule. Have students silently consider what the rule might be and make suggestions. As students guess a rule, first confirm that their rule names the correct fraction of the group of students; then confirm whether or not it is the rule you had chosen. Here is an example:

Alex says that one half of the group is wearing a watch. Is that true? Are one half of the students in the group wearing watches? . . . Unfortunately, that's not my rule! Are there any other guesses?

Step 3 Discuss the fraction identified. Once the rule has been identified, discuss the fraction. Does the fraction have any equivalents? For example, if 5 of 10 people fit the rule, and the fraction is $\frac{1}{2}$, what equivalent fraction would also name that portion of the group? $\left(\frac{5}{10}\right)$

What landmark fraction is the fraction close to? Is it larger or smaller than that landmark fraction? For example, if 13 of 25 students fit the rule and the fraction is close to $\frac{1}{2}$, is it more or less than $\frac{1}{2}$? (*more*) Also identify the fraction of the group that *does not* fit the rule.

Variation

Guess My Rule with Objects

Materials

• A collection of objects, such as buttons, Power Polygons, desk supplies (paper clips, tacks, clips, etc.)

Follow the same procedure as in the basic activity but use a collection of objects instead of a group of students. Objects might be classified by attributes such as shape, how many holes in a button, color, use (things that keep paper together such as paper clips or staples), and so on.

Number Puzzles

Students work in pairs to identify the number or numbers that fit three given clues. Each clue gives one characteristic of the number, which might include a property such as being prime or square, information about the factors or the multiples of the number, or something about the magnitude of the number.

Math Focus Points

Students use reasoning and their knowledge of the properties and the relationships of numbers to find a given number.

◆ Identifying prime, square, even, and odd numbers

◆ Determining if one number is a factor or multiple of another

Number Puzzles is introduced in Session 2.2 in Unit 1, *Number Puzzles and Multiple Towers;* it also appears in Unit 7, *How Many People? How Many Teams?*

Materials

- Resource Masters M35–M43 (Unit 1) or M16–M24 (Unit 7), *Number Puzzle Clue Cards* (cut apart and divided into sets A, B, and C)

- Blank paper

- Calculators

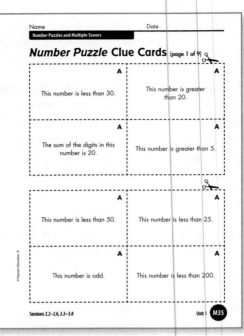

Name _____ Date _____

Number Puzzles and Multiple Towers

Number Puzzle **Clue Cards** (page 1 of 9)

A	A
This number is less than 30.	This number is greater than 20.
A	A
The sum of the digits in this number is 20.	This number is greater than 5.
A	A
This number is less than 50.	This number is less than 25.
A	A
This number is odd.	This number is less than 200.

Sessions 2.2–2.6, 3.3–3.8   Unit 1 M35

▲ **Resource Masters, Unit 1 M35**

Basic Activity

Step 1 Draw three cards, one from each set—A, B, and C. Read, or have a volunteer read, each individual clue aloud. Ask students to interpret the clue and, if necessary, to restate it in their own words. For example, if the card reads, *This number is a multiple of 4,* students might say, "You can count by 4s to get that number," or "You can divide the number by 4 evenly." Record the clue in some way on the board or overhead (e.g., multiple of 4). Continue in this way until all three clues have been recorded.

Step 2 Students work in pairs to identify numbers that fit all three clues. Give students 3–5 minutes to work with their partners to find numbers that fit all three clues. Allow them to use calculators or other materials (grid paper, square tiles, etc.) to help them determine possible answers.

Step 3 Ask for volunteers to explain their solutions. Call the class back together and ask students to volunteer answers. Record each answer on the board or overhead. Ask students to explain their individual strategies:

How did you find the solution?

Which clue did you start with? Why?

Was there any clue that was (wasn't) helpful? Why?

As students explain their solutions, ask the rest of the class if they agree. If students do not agree, have them explain why. For example,

The second clue says that the number is a multiple of 2, so that means it is an even number. Twenty-five is odd, so it won't work.

Step 4 If the clues result in an impossible puzzle, ask the class to modify one of the clues. Because the cards are drawn randomly, it is possible that either the number puzzle will be impossible to solve or that there will be an infinite number of answers. When this happens, ask students to modify the puzzle to make a handful of solutions possible. They can do this by eliminating a clue, adding a clue, or rewriting one of the existing clues. For example, here is a puzzle with no solution:

This number has two digits.

This number is a multiple of 2.

This number is prime.

Ask students how they could modify one of the clues to give a possible answer. One solution would be to eliminate the first clue; then the puzzle would have one answer (2). Another possibility would be to change the last clue in some way to limit the number of solutions (e.g., This number is less than 20).

Here is a puzzle with too many solutions:

This number is more than 100.

This number is a square number.

This number is a multiple of 4.

Possible modifications for this puzzle include adding a rule, for example: This number is less than 500. (Then the possible answers are 144, 196, 256, 324, and 400.) Another modification would be rewriting a clue. The first clue, for example, could be written as follows: This number is less than 100. (Then the possible answers are 4, 16, 36, and 64.)

Variations

Draw Three, Trade One

In this variation, if the original cards result in an impossible puzzle, students decide which of the three cards should be removed, and a new card from the same set is selected.

Random Clues

In this variation, the clues are not separated into three sets. Combine all the clues and draw the first three cards from the deck. This variation has greater potential for resulting in impossible puzzles, and it provides more opportunities to analyze, discuss, and modify clues.

Practicing Place Value

Students practice reading and writing numbers up to 100,000. Then students add 10 and multiples of 10 to or subtract 10 and multiples of 10 from the given numbers. Students discuss how the values of the digits change in each equation. Students develop flexibility in decomposing numbers as they break 3-digit numbers into hundreds, tens, and ones in various ways and demonstrate their equivalence.

Math Focus Points

Students focus on how numbers are composed and how written numerals relate to the quantity they represent.

◆ Recognizing and interpreting the value of each digit in 4- and 5-digit numbers

◆ Finding different combinations of a number, using only 1,000s, 100s, 10s, and 1s and recognizing their equivalence (e.g., 1 hundred, 3 tens, and 7 ones = 1 hundred, 2 tens, and 17 ones = 13 tens and 7 ones = 12 tens and 17 ones; etc.)

◆ Reading and writing numbers up to 100,000

◆ Adding multiples of 10 to and subtracting multiples of 10 from 4- and 5-digit numbers

◆ Reading and writing decimal fractions and decimal numbers

◆ Adding tenths or hundredths to, and subtracting them from, decimal fractions and decimal numbers

Practicing Place Value is introduced in Session 1.3 in Unit 3, *Thousands of Miles, Thousands of Seats;* it also appears in Unit 6, *Decimals on Grids and Number Lines;* and in Unit 8, *Growth Patterns.*

Materials

• Blank paper and pencil

Basic Activity

Step 1 **Write or say a number.** Your choice of number will depend on the size of the numbers your students are working on or need work with. Alternate between writing the numbers on the board and reading them aloud. For example, write 12,435 or say "twelve thousand, four hundred thirty-five."

Step 2 **Students say or write the number.** Students share with a partner. Give all students an opportunity to read, write, and say this number correctly. Ask a volunteer to say or write the number for the whole class.

Step 3 **Add or subtract multiples of 10.** Write or say a series of addition and/or subtraction problems, adding or subtracting multiples of 10 (tens, hundreds, thousands, ten thousands, etc.) to the starting number. For example,

What is 12,435 + 2,000? 12,435 + 20,000? 12,435 + 4,000? 12,345 + 40,000? 12,345 + 6,000? 12,345 + 60,000?

or

What is 12,435 + 2,000? 12,435 − 2,000? 12,435 + 4,000? 12,435 − 4,000?

Step 4 **Students mentally solve the problem.** As students share their solutions, write the equations (e.g., 12,435 + 2,000 = 14,435; 12,435 + 20,000 = 32,435), or have a student write them, on the board.

Step 5 **Discuss place value.** Ask students to compare each sum or difference with the starting number (e.g., for the problem 12,435 + 2,000, compare 14,435 and 12,435). Ask:

What was the effect of adding the multiple to or subtracting the multiple from the starting number? Which places in the two numbers have the same digits? Which places do not? Why?

Step 6 **If time remains, pose additional similar problems.**

Variations

Decimal Numbers

In this variation, the basic procedure stays the same, but students practice adding multiples of 10 to, and subtracting multiples of 10 from, decimal numbers (e.g., 356.4 + 20, 356.4 − 20, 356.4 + 200, 356.4 − 200). Alternatively, students practice adding tenths and hundredths to, and subtracting them from, decimal numbers (e.g., 356.4 + 0.1, 356.4 + 0.3, 356.4 + 1.4). As with the basic procedure, have students compare each sum or difference with the starting number and identify how the places have changed and why.

Decimal Fractions

The teacher writes a decimal fraction (a number less than 1) on the board, such as 0.4. Students practice saying the number, using both common ways of reading decimals (e.g., "four tenths" or "zero point four"). Ask students questions like the following:

What is 2 tenths more than this number?

What is 2 hundredths more than this number?

What is 1 hundredth less?

How Many 10s? How Many 100s? How Many 1,000s?

In this variation, students decompose numbers by place. Doing so involves more than just naming the number in each place. It includes understanding, for example, that while 335 is 3 hundreds, 3 tens, and 5 ones, it is also 2 hundreds, 13 tens, and 5 ones; or 1 hundred, 23 tens, and 5 ones; or 33 tens and 5 ones; and so on.

Step 1 Write or say a number. Write a number on the board (or say it and have students write it). For example:

12,435

Step 2 Ask: "How many groups of _____ (10, 100, 1,000, etc.) are in the number?" For example, ask students how many thousands are in 12,435. If students think that 2 thousands is the only answer, ask them to consider a context, such as the 10,000 chart or money.

If our 10,000 chart went past 10,000, how many rectangles of 1,000 would we have?

or

If this were money, how many thousand dollar bills would we have if we had $12,435?

Help students realize that there are 12 thousands in this number.

Step 3 Pose additional questions. Using the same example number, ask students to fill in the blanks in the following expressions for 12,435 and explain how they figured out each value:

_____ thousands + 4 hundreds + 3 tens + 5 ones

11 thousands + _____ hundreds + 35 ones

8 thousands + _____ hundreds + 35 ones

Then ask students to make up five different combinations of place values that equal 12,435 (e.g., 12 thousands, 40 tens, 35 ones; 10 thousands, 24 hundreds, 35 ones; 124 hundreds, 35 ones; etc.).

Quick Images

In this activity, students visualize and analyze images of geometric figures. After briefly viewing an image of a two-dimensional (2-D) design or three-dimensional (3-D) structure, students either draw it or build it from the mental image they formed during the brief viewing. They might see it as a whole ("it looks like a box, three cubes long and two cubes high") or decompose it into memorable parts ("it looks like four triangles—right side up, then upside down, then right side up, then upside down"). This activity provides students with practice in developing spatial skills and in using language to communicate about spatial relationships.

Math Focus Points

Students visualize and reconstruct geometric images (of 2-D geometric designs or 3-D cube structures), either as a whole or by decomposing them into memorable parts.

◆ Organizing and analyzing visual images

◆ Developing language and concepts needed to communicate about spatial relationships

Quick Images is introduced in Session 1.1 in Unit 1, *Number Puzzles and Multiple Towers;* it also appears in Unit 2, *Prisms and Pyramids;* and in Unit 5, *Measuring Polygons.*

Materials

• Overhead projector

• Transparencies T1–T12, T25–T29, T54–T57, *Quick Images*

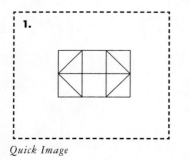

Quick Image

Basic Activity

Step 1 Flash an image for 3 seconds. It is important to show the figure for as close to 3 seconds as possible. If you show it too long, students will draw or build from the figure rather than from their mental image of it; if you show it too briefly, students will not have sufficient time to form a mental image. Students quickly learn to study the figure carefully while it is visible so they can draw or build it from their mental images.

Step 2 Students draw or build what they saw. Give students a few minutes with the relevant materials (paper and pencil, cubes) to draw or construct a figure that matches the mental image they formed. When you see that most students have finished working, proceed to step 3.

Step 3 Flash the image again for 3 seconds, this time for revision. After showing the image for another 3 seconds, students revise their drawings or buildings according to what they see in this second viewing. It is essential to provide enough time here, before a third showing, for most students to complete their attempts at drawing or building. While they may not have completed their figures, they should have done all they can until they see the image displayed again. When student work subsides, proceed to step 4.

Step 4 Show the image a third and final time. This time leave the image visible so that all students can complete or revise their solutions.

Step 5 Discuss the mental images students formed. Students explain the different ways they saw the figure as they looked at it on successive "flashes." Encourage students to explain what relationships they used in decomposing the figure.

Variations

Quick Images: Seeing Numbers

Quick Images: Seeing Numbers is introduced in Session 1.1 in Unit 1, *Number Puzzles and Multiple Towers.*

Materials

- Transparencies T1–T12, *Quick Images: Seeing Numbers*

- Paper and pencil

Math Focus Point

◈ Writing multiplication and division equations to represent the total number of shapes in a pattern

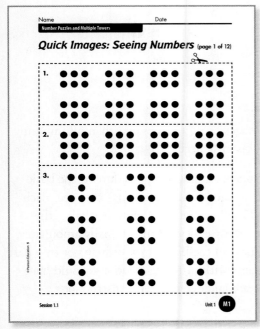

▲ Resource Masters, Unit 1 M1; Transparencies, T1

Following the procedure in the basic activity, students determine the number of dots in an image and write an equation to represent how they organized their counting. Some students may want to draw a mental image of the arrangement to get a clearer picture of it. To help students describe their mental images and write an equation, ask questions such as the following:

How were the dots arranged?

How many dots were in each group?

How many groups were there?

Quick Images: 2-D

Quick Images: 2-D is introduced in Session 1.1 in Unit 5, *Measuring Polygons.*

Materials

- Transparencies T54–T57, *Quick Images: 2-D*

- Blank paper and pencil

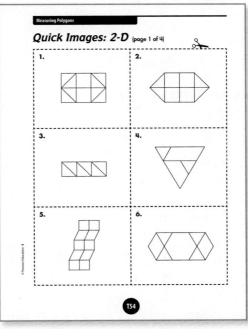

▲ Resource Masters, Unit 5 M5; Transparencies, T54

Math Focus Points

◆ Decomposing images of 2-D shapes and then recombining them to make a given design

Following the procedure for the basic activity, students use paper and pencil to draw the 2-D designs they see.

When talking about what they saw in successive flashes, many students will say things like "I saw four triangles in a row." For students having difficulty, suggest the following:

Each design is made from familiar geometric shapes. Find these shapes and try to figure out how they are put together.

As students describe their figures, you can introduce the correct geometric terms for component shapes. As you use these terms naturally in class discussion, students will soon begin to recognize and use them more frequently and accurately.

Quick Images: 3-D

Quick Images: 3-D is introduced in Session 1.1 in Unit 2, *Prisms and Pyramids.*

Materials

• Transparencies T25–T29, *Quick Images: 3-D*

• Connecting cubes (15–20 per student)

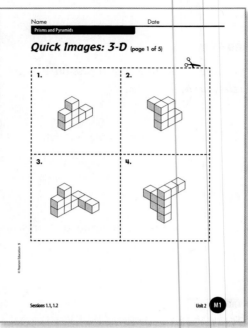

▲ Resource Masters, Unit 2 M1; Transparencies, T25

Math Focus Point

◆ Decomposing images of 3-D shapes and then recombining them to make a given structure

For this version, students follow the procedure in the basic procedure to build images of cube buildings they see. Each student will need 15–20 connecting cubes. Several of the cube figures on the transparency are intentionally ambiguous, as some unseen cubes "in the back" may or may not be a part of the figure. Students with differing solutions should have the chance to compare and defend their constructions.

Quick Survey

Quick Survey gives students many opportunities to quickly collect, graph, describe, and interpret data about themselves and the world around them. Students collect data to investigate a question about themselves. The data can be organized as a line plot, a list, a table, or a bar graph. Then students describe what they can derive from the data, generate some new questions, and, if appropriate, make predictions about what will happen the next time they collect the same data.

Math Focus Points

Students collect, organize, describe, and interpret data.

◆ Describing important features of the data

◆ Interpreting and posing questions about the data

Quick Survey is introduced in Session 2.1 in Unit 5, *Measuring Polygons;* it also appears in Unit 9, *How Long Can You Stand on One Foot?*

Materials

• Chart paper or overhead projector

• Marking pen

Basic Activity

Step 1 Choose a question. Use the question suggested or use your own question, which can also be provided by the students. Make sure the question involves data that students know or can observe. Here are some examples: How many buttons are you wearing today? What is the best thing you ate yesterday? Are you wearing shoes or sneakers or sandals? How did you get to school today? What is your favorite fruit? What do you usually eat for breakfast?

Step 2 Quickly collect and display the data. Use a list, a table, a line plot, or a bar graph. For example, a bar graph for data about how students get to school could look something like this:

Step 3 Ask students to describe the data. What do they notice? For data that have a *numerical order* (e.g., How many buttons do you have today? How many people live in your house? How many months until your birthday?), ask questions like these:

Are the data spread out or close together?

What are the highest and lowest values?

Where do most of the data seem to fall?

What seems typical or usual for this class?

For data in categories (e.g., What is your favorite book? How do you get to school? What month is your birthday?), ask questions like these:

Which categories have a lot of data? . . . few data? . . . none?

Is there a way to categorize the data differently to get other information?

Step 4 Ask students to interpret and predict.

Why do you think that the data came out this way?

Does anything about the data surprise you?

Do you think we would get similar data if we collected it tomorrow? next week? in another class? with adults?

Step 5 List any new questions. Keep a running list of questions you can use for further data collection and analysis. You many want to ask some of these questions again.

Math Note

Graphs About Favorites

If students take surveys about "favorites"—for example, flavor of ice cream, breakfast cereal, book, color—or other data that fall into categories, the graphs are often flat and uninteresting. There is not too much to say, for example, about a graph like this:

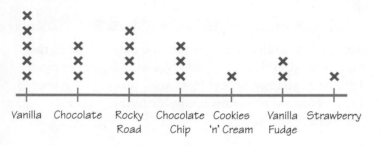

Favorite Ice Cream Flavor

It is more interesting for students to group their results into more descriptive categories so that they can see other things about the data. In this case, even though vanilla seems to be the favorite in this graph, another way for grouping the data seems to show that flavors with some chocolate in them are really the favorites:

Flavors with chocolate: 𝍠𝍠 𝍠𝍠 𝍠𝍠𝍠

Flavors without chocolate: 𝍠𝍠 𝍠

Variations

Data from Home

Students might collect data that involves asking questions or making observations at home. What time do your brothers and sisters go to bed? How many states (or how many countries) have you visited? How many cousins do you have? Students bring in their answers to use in the class activity.

Data from Another Class or Other Teachers

Depending on your school situation, you may be able to assign students to collect data from other classrooms or other teachers. Students are always interested in surveying others about questions that interest them, such as this question for teachers: When you were in fifth grade, what did you like best about school?

PART 5

Technology in *Investigations*

Preview

The *Investigations* curriculum incorporates two forms of technology: calculators and computers. Calculators are assumed to be standard mathematical tools, available for student use as appropriate. Computers, on the other hand, are explicitly linked to one curriculum unit at each grade level through software that is provided with the curriculum.

Using Calculators with the Curriculum

Students should become comfortable using a basic calculator as a tool that is common in their homes and communities. Increasingly, sophisticated calculators are being developed and used in settings ranging from high school mathematics courses to science, business, and construction. Students need to learn how to use the calculator effectively and appropriately as a tool, just as they need to learn to read a clock, interpret a map, measure with a ruler, or use coins. They should use calculators for sensible purposes—just as you would do—not as a replacement for mental calculations or for pencil and paper calculations they are learning to do. Encourage students to use calculators to double-check calculations, as an aid if they have many calculations to carry out outside of math class, or to solve problems for which they can think out a solution but don't yet have the experience to carry out the computation.

Calculators are recommended for a few specific activities in curriculum units. For most of the work on number and operations, students are using their own representations and reasoning to solve problems as they develop computational fluency. Calculators might sometimes be used for double-checking, although students should also be able to double-check their work without a calculator.

Look for situations in the classroom when the purpose of the mathematical activity is not the development of computational fluency and when the numbers and calculations are beyond the students' skills in written or mental computation. These situations provide opportunities for students to practice estimating reasonable results and then carrying out the calculation with a calculator.

For example, students could work to find the total of a class book order. Pose some questions to help them estimate first:

Will the total be over $50? between $50 and $100? between $100 and $150?

Help them to think about grouping the book to estimate:

How many of the books cost close to $1.00 each?

Then students can carry out the complete calculation with a calculator.

Ask questions to help students learn good practices with the calculator:

How are you keeping track of which books you have added and which you still need to add?

Is your result reasonable according to your estimate?

How can you double-check the calculator result (for example, by subtracting off each book)?

Students enjoy using what they perceive as an adult tool. Investigating with the calculator gives students an opportunity to notice mathematical patterns and to ask questions about mathematical symbols. For example, in a second-grade class, students were dividing lots of numbers by 2, which led to a discussion of the meaning of 0.5. In a fourth-grade class, some students became intrigued with the square root sign. The teacher challenged them to systematically keep track of the results of applying the square root symbol to whole numbers, starting with 1, and to come up with an idea about its meaning.

The calculator is an efficient tool for many purposes in life, and students should learn to use it sensibly, knowing that using it well depends on the user's correct analysis and organization of the problem, comparing its results with reasonable estimates, and double-checking.

Introducing and Managing the *LogoPaths* Software in Grade 5

LogoPaths Software is provided as a component of the *Investigations* curriculum. While using this software is optional, we recommend its use if you have computers either in your classroom or in your school's computer lab. The *Software Support Reference Guide* provides a complete description of the software and instructions for using the software activities.

The *LogoPaths* Software is formally introduced in Grade 5, Unit 5, *Measuring Polygons.* However, if you can give students some experience with the software early in the year, *before* Unit 5, they will be better prepared to use it to solve the specific problems in that unit.

Therefore, we recommend that you start using the software outside of math time, starting with Unit 2, *Prisms and Pyramids,* by reviewing *Mazes*—a game they played in Grade 4 that uses combinations of forward and backward moves and turns of varying degrees to move a turtle through a maze—and using the *Free Explore* option to experiment with drawing figures with different numbers of sides, and a variety of side lengths, and angle sizes.

In Unit 5, you will find suggestions for introducing the *LogoPaths* games and activities during specific sessions and integrating them into your Math Workshops. The software activities extend and deepen the mathematical ideas that are emphasized in this curriculum unit. In some cases, they allow students to work with geometric figures and with angles in ways that are not possible in the noncomputer activities.

Options for Introducing the *LogoPaths* Software

- *Computer lab:* If you have a computer laboratory with one computer for each pair of students, the entire class can become familiar with the computer activities at the same time. In this case, you will not need to devote time during math class to introduce the new software activity. Once an activity has been introduced, students can do it either during Math Workshop (if you have classroom computers) or during their scheduled lab time.

- *Large projection screen:* If you have a large projection screen, you can introduce the software activities to the whole class during a math session, immediately before Math Workshop or at another time of the day.

- *Small groups of students:* With fewer classroom computers, you can introduce the activities to small groups either before or during Math Workshop. These students can then be paired and become peer "teachers" of the software.

Regardless of the number of computers available, students generally benefit from working on these activities in pairs. This not only maximizes computer resources but also encourages students to consult, monitor, and teach one another. Generally, more than two students at one computer find it difficult to share. You may need to monitor computer use more closely than the other Math Workshop choices to ensure that all students get sufficient computer time. Each pair should spend at least 15–20 minutes at the computer for each activity.

Managing the Computer Environment

Students should be using the *LogoPaths* Software consistently throughout Unit 5 and periodically the rest of the school year. If you have daily access to a computer lab, you might take advantage of this to supplement your regular math class. If your school has a computer teacher, you might collaborate with that teacher to have students work on *LogoPaths* activities during some of their scheduled lab time.

More typically, a classroom will have a small number of computers. With computers in the classroom, pairs of students can cycle through the software activities during Math Workshop, just as they cycle through the other choices. Three to five classroom computers is ideal, but even with only one or two, students can have a successful computer experience. When you have fewer computers, find additional computer time for students throughout the day, outside of math.

Using *LogoPaths* All Year

After the formal introduction of the software in Unit 5, subsequent units each include a Technology Note with suggestions and reminders for ongoing use of the software during the rest of the year. Continued experience with *LogoPaths* allows students to become increasingly fluent in the mechanics of the software itself and able to better focus on the mathematical ideas of the game and activities.

Throughout Grade 5, the Resource Masters include some designed for continued student work with activities such as *Rhombuses and Parallelograms, Triangles,* and *Polygon Pairs.* Students should also continue using the *Free Explore* activities that offer experiences with the properties of two-dimensional (2-D) shapes, including their angles.

Introducing the *LogoPaths* Activities

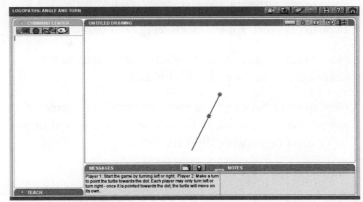

In your first introduction of the *Angle and Turn Game,* show students the following:

- How to open the *Angle and Turn Game* by clicking on it once

- How to enter right and left turn commands in degrees of any amount (e.g. **rt 50, lt 110, rt 390**)

- How to use the *Turtle Turner* tool

In your first introduction of the *Triangles* and *Rhombuses and Parallelograms* activities, show students the following:

- How to open *Free Explore* by clicking on it once

- How to enter forward and backward commands in the Command Center (e.g., **fd 82**, **bk 125**)

- How to enter right and left turn commands in degrees of any amount (e.g., rt **50**, lt **110**) (Note that move and turn input must be between -999 and 999.)

- How to delete a command they wish to change

- How to use the *Label Lengths* and *Label Turns* tools

- How to use the *Turtle Turner* and *Ruler* tools

- How to use the **ht** (hide turtle) and **st** (show turtle) commands

- How to use the *Teach Tool* to make a procedure out of a set of commands in the Command Center. You will be asked to give it a name, and the commands will be moved to the Teach Window in the proper format for a procedure.

In your first introduction of the *Polygon Pairs* activity, show students the following:

- How to open *Polygon Pairs* by clicking on it once

- How to pick a specific *Polygon Pairs* puzzle

- How to use the *Label Lengths* and *Label Turns* tools to compare the polygons within each pair

- How to use the *Overlay* procedures to compare the polygons within each pair

You can introduce more of the tools available in *LogoPaths* as students indicate interest and the need to use them.

- Students can use the penup (**pu**) and pendown (**pd**) commands to tell the turtle to draw as it moves. Type **pu** in the Command Center to move without drawing. Type **pd** for the turtle to draw as it moves.

- The repeat command tells the turtle to repeat a set of commands a specified number of times. The first input is the number of times to repeat, and the second is a list of commands enclosed in square brackets. For example, to repeat a forward move and a right turn three times, students might type **repeat 3 [fd 100 rt 90]**.

- Students can change the color, shape, and size of the turtle and the line it draws using the turtle features panel . Other features of how the turtle works (e.g., its speed) can be changed in the preferences panel .

- Further information about commands, tools, and buttons can be found in the online help .

It is likely that many students will discover other tools and their uses on their own as they spend more time working with the software. Encourage them to share their discoveries with one another.

Saving Student Work

If you want to discuss students' work later, they should either print it (if your computers are connected to a printer) or save their work on a disk. For information about printing or saving to a disk, see the *Software Support Reference Guide* contained in your curriculum guide package.

PART 6

Professional Development

Teacher Notes in *Investigations*

Teacher Notes are one of the most important professional development tools in *Investigations*. Each curriculum unit contains a collection of Teacher Notes that offer information about the mathematical content of that unit and how students learn it.

In this section of *Implementing Investigations in Grade 5,* you will find a set of Teacher Notes that addresses topics and issues applicable to the curriculum as a whole rather than to specific curriculum units.

These Teacher Notes provide important background about approaches to mathematics teaching and learning, about critical features of the mathematics classroom, and about how to develop an inclusive mathematics community in which all students participate. You can benefit from reading these notes, either individually or as the basis for discussion in teacher study groups, before starting to use the curriculum. Alternatively, you can read these notes gradually throughout the year while you are using the curriculum in your classroom. These brief essays take on new resonance and meaning as you have more experience with student learning and the *Investigations* curriculum. Plan to return to this collection periodically to review the ideas and reflect on the implications for classroom practice.

A complete list of the Teacher Note titles from each of the nine curriculum units is included on pages 68–69.

Computational Fluency and Place Value

Computational fluency includes accuracy, flexibility, and efficiency. When fluency with a particular operation is achieved, students can look at the problem as a whole, choose a solution strategy that they can carry out easily without becoming bogged down or losing track of their steps, use their strategy to solve the problem accurately, recognize whether the result is reasonable, and double-check their work. Students who are fluent have a repertoire that includes mental strategies, strategies in which only intermediate steps are jotted down while other steps are carried out mentally, and strategies that require a complete written solution. They are flexible in their choice of algorithm or procedure, and they can use one method to check another.

Developing computational fluency with whole numbers is central to the elementary curriculum. This development includes the building blocks of computation:

• Understanding the base-ten number system and its place value notation

• Understanding the meaning of the operations and their relationships

• Knowing the basic addition and multiplication number combinations (the "facts") and their counterparts for subtraction and division

• Estimating reasonable results

• Interpreting problems embedded in contexts and applying the operations correctly to these problems

• Learning, practicing, and consolidating accurate and efficient strategies for computing

• Developing curiosity about numbers and operations, their characteristics, and how they work

• Learning to articulate, represent, and justify generalizations

At each grade level, computational fluency looks different. Students are progressing in learning the meaning of the four

arithmetic operations with whole numbers, developing methods grounded in this meaning, and gradually solving problems of greater difficulty through the grades. At each grade level, benchmarks for whole number computation indicate what is expected of all students by the end of each curriculum unit and each grade, although work at each grade level goes beyond these benchmarks. Gradually, approaches to problems become more efficient, flexible, and accurate. For example, in Grade 1, many students begin the year adding by direct modeling of the problem with objects and counting the sum by ones. By the end of the year, students are expected to start with one of the quantities and count on the other, and for some combinations students "just know" the sum or use known combinations to solve others ("I know $4 + 4 = 8$, so $4 + 5 = 9$"). In Grade 4, many students start the year solving some multiplication problems by skip counting, but by the end of the year, they are expected to solve multidigit multiplication problems such as 34×68 by breaking problems into subproblems, based on the distributive property.

$$30 \times 60 = 1800$$
$$30 \times 8 = 240$$
$$4 \times 60 = 240$$
$$4 \times 8 = 32$$
$$4$$
$$\overline{2312}$$

68 round to 70

$34 + 34 = 68$

$70 \times 4 = 280$
$70 \times 30 = 2100$

$2380 - 68 = 2312$

Sample Student Work

Understanding the Base-Ten Number System

Learning about whole number computation is closely connected to learning about the base-ten number system. The base-ten number system is a "place value" system. That is, any numeral, say 2, can represent different values, depending on where it appears in a written number: it can represent 2 ones, 2 tens, 2 hundreds, 2 thousands, as well as 2 tenths, 2 hundredths, and so forth. Understanding this place value system requires coordinating the way we write the numerals that represent a particular number (e.g., 217) and the way we name numbers in words (e.g., two hundred seventeen) with how those symbols represent quantities.

The heart of this work is relating written numerals to the quantity and to how the quantity is composed. It builds from work on tens and ones in Grades 1 and 2 to a focus on numbers in the hundreds and thousands in Grade 3, and work with numbers in the ten thousands, hundred thousands, and beyond in Grades 4 and 5. Knowing place value is not simply a matter of saying that 217 "has 2 hundreds, 1 ten, and 7 ones," which students can easily learn to do by following a pattern without attaching much meaning to what they are saying. Students must learn to visualize how 217 is built up from hundreds, tens, and ones, in a way that helps them relate its value to other quantities. Understanding the place value of a number such as 217 entails knowing, for example, that 217 is closer to 200 than to 300, that it is 100 more than 117, that it is 17 more than 200, that it is 3 less than 220, and that it is composed of 21 tens and 7 ones.

A thorough understanding of the base-ten number system is one of the critical building blocks for developing computational fluency. Understanding place value is at the heart of estimating and computing. For example, consider adding two different quantities to 32:

$32 + 30 =$ _____

$32 + 3 =$ _____

How much will 32 increase in each case? Students think about how the first sum will now have 6 tens, but the ones will not change, whereas in the second sum, the ones will change, but the tens remain the same. Adding three *tens* almost doubles 32, while adding three *ones* increases its value by a small amount. Considering the place value of numbers that are being added, subtracted, multiplied, or divided provides the basis for developing a reasonable estimate of the result.

The composition of numbers from multiples of 1, 10, 100, 1,000, and so forth, is the basis for most of the strategies students adopt for whole number operations. Students' computational algorithms and procedures depend on knowing how to decompose numbers and knowing the effects of operating with multiples of 10. For example, one of the most common algorithms for addition is adding by place. Each number is decomposed into ones, tens, hundreds, and so forth; these parts are then combined. For example,

$326 + 493$

$300 + 400 = 700$

$20 + 90 = 110$

$6 + 3 = 9$

$700 + 110 + 9 = 819$

To carry out this algorithm fluently, students must know a great deal about place value, not just how to decompose numbers. They must also be able to apply their knowledge of single-digit sums such as $3 + 4$ and $2 + 9$ to sums such as $300 + 400$ and $20 + 90$. In other words, they know how to interpret the place value of numbers *as they operate with them*—in this case, that just as 2 ones plus 9 ones equals 11 ones, 2 tens plus 9 tens equals 11 tens, or 110.

As with addition, algorithms for multidigit multiplication also depend on knowing how the place value of numbers is interpreted as numbers are multiplied. Again, students must understand how they can apply knowledge of single-digit combinations such as 3×4 to solve problems such as 36×42.

For example,

36×42

$30 \times 40 = 1,200$

$30 \times 2 = 60$

$6 \times 40 = 240$

$6 \times 2 = 12$

$1,200 + 240 + 60 + 12 = 1,512$

Students gradually learn how a knowledge of 3×4 helps them solve 30×4, 3×40, 30×40, 3×400, and so forth.

Building Computational Fluency Over Time

There is a tremendous amount of work to do in the area of numbers and operations in Grades K–5.

- Kindergartners and first graders are still working on coordinating written and spoken numbers with their quantitative meaning.

- Second graders are uncovering the relationship between 10 ones and 1 ten and between 10 tens and 1 hundred.

- Third graders are immersed in how the properties of multiplication differ from the properties of addition.

- Fourth and fifth graders are solving multidigit problems and becoming flexible in their use of a number of algorithms.

This list provides only a brief glimpse of how much work there is to do in these grades.

Students gain computational fluency in each operation through several years of careful development. Extended time across several grades is spent on each operation. Students build computational fluency with small numbers as they learn about the meaning and properties of the operation.

Then they gradually expand their work to more difficult problems as they develop, analyze, compare, and practice general methods.

Let's use subtraction as an example of this process:

- In Kindergarten and Grade 1, students solve subtraction problems by modeling the action of subtraction.

- By Grade 2, students are articulating and using the inverse relationship between addition and subtraction to solve problems like the following: "If I have 10 cookies, how many more cookies do I need to bake so I have 24?"

- During Grades 2 and 3, students become fluent with the subtraction "facts" and model and solve a variety of types of subtraction problems, including comparison and missing part problems. By Grade 3, as students' understanding of the base-ten number system grows, they use their understanding of place value to solve problems with larger numbers.

- In Grades 3 and 4, students articulate, represent, and justify important generalizations about subtraction. For example, if you add the same amount to (or subtract it from) each number in a subtraction expression, the difference does not change, as in the equation $483 - 197 = 486 - 200$. In these grades, students also choose one or two procedures, practice them, and expand their command of these procedures with multidigit numbers.

- In Grades 4 and 5, as their fluency with subtraction increases, students analyze and compare strategies for solving subtraction problems. Because they are fluent with more "transparent" algorithms for subtraction in which the place value of the numbers is clear, they are now in a position to appreciate the shortcut notation of the U.S. traditional regrouping algorithm for subtraction, analyze how it works, and compare it to other algorithms. (See the Teacher Note, Computational Algorithms and Methods.)

This account gives only a glimpse of the work involved in understanding subtraction across the grades. Each operation has a similar complexity. It is critical that the time and depth required for the careful development of ideas is devoted to this strand. For this reason, in each of Grades 1–4, there are four units spread throughout the year that focus on whole numbers, operations, and the base-ten number system. In Kindergarten, three units focus on counting, quantity, and modeling addition and subtraction. In Grade 5, because of the increased emphasis on rational numbers, three units focus on whole numbers and two units focus on fractions, decimals, and percents. The whole number units within each grade build on each other in a careful sequence.

As you work with your students on whole number computation, here are some questions to keep in mind as you assess their progress toward computational fluency [adapted from Russell, 2000, p. 158]:

- Do students know and draw on basic facts and other number relationships?

- Do students use and understand the structure of the base-ten number system? For example, do students know the result of adding 100 to 2,340 or multiplying 40×500?

- Do students recognize related problems that can help with the problem?

- Do students use relationships among operations?

- Do students know what each number and numeral in the problem means (including subproblems)?

- Can students explain why the steps being used actually work?

- Do students have a clear way to record and keep track of their procedures?

- Do students have more than one approach for solving problems in each operation? Can they determine which problems lend themselves to different methods?

Supporting Computational Fluency Across the Curriculum

Work in the other content areas also connects to and supports the work on computational fluency in the number and operations units. For example, an emphasis on the foundations of algebra across the grades opens up important opportunities to strengthen work with numbers and operations. Within the number and operations units themselves, articulation, representation, and justification of general claims about the operations (an aspect of early algebraic thinking) strengthen students' understanding of the operations (see the Teacher Note, Foundations of Algebra in the Elementary Grades, and the Algebra Connections essay in each of the number and operations units). The work with functions provides interesting problem contexts in which students' work on ratio and on constant rates of change connect to and support their work on multiplication (see the Teacher Note, Foundations of Algebra in the Elementary Grades, and the Algebra Connections essay in each of the patterns, functions, and change units). Geometry and measurement units also provide contexts in which students revisit multiplication. Finally, the Classroom Routines (in Grades K–3) and Ten-Minute Math (in Grades 3–5) provide ongoing, regular practice of estimation and computation.

Reference

Russell, S. J. (2000). Developing computational fluency with whole numbers. *Teaching Children Mathematics 7*, 154–158.

Computational Algorithms and Methods

In the elementary grades, a central part of students' work is learning about addition, subtraction, multiplication, and division and becoming fluent and flexible in solving whole number computation problems. In the *Investigations* curriculum, students use methods and algorithms in which they can see clearly the steps of their solution and focus on the mathematical sense of what they are doing. They use and compare several different methods to deepen their understanding of the properties of the operations and to develop flexibility in solving problems. They practice methods for each operation so that they can use them efficiently to solve problems.

What Is an Algorithm?

An algorithm is a series of well-defined steps used to solve a certain class of problem (for example, all addition problems). Often, the sequence of steps is repeated with successive parts of the problem. For example, here is an example of an addition algorithm:

$$249 + 674$$
$$200 + 600 = 800$$
$$40 + 70 = 110$$
$$9 + 4 = 13$$
$$800 + 110 + 13 = 923$$

Written instructions for this algorithm might begin as follows:

1. Find the left-most place represented in the addends and add all the amounts in that place.

2. Move one place to the right and add all the amounts in that place in all the addends.

3. Repeat step 2 until all parts of all addends have been added.

4. Add the sums of each place.

To specify these instructions, as if we were going to teach them to a computer, we would have more work to do to make them even more specific and precise. For example, how is step 4 carried out? Should each place be added separately again and then combined? In practice, when students and adults use this algorithm, the partial sums that must be added in step 4 are generally easy enough to add mentally, as they are in this problem, although occasionally one might again break up some of the numbers.

Algorithms like this one, once understood and practiced, are general methods that can be used for a whole class of problems. The adding by place algorithm, for example, can be generalized for use with any addition problem. As students' knowledge of the number system expands, they learn to apply this algorithm to, for example, larger numbers or to decimals. Students also learn how to use clear and concise notation, to carry out some steps mentally, and to record those intermediate steps needed so that they can keep track of the solution process.

Nonalgorithmic Methods for Computing with Whole Numbers

Students also learn methods for computing with whole numbers that are not algorithmic—that is, one cannot completely specify the steps for carrying them out, and they do not generally involve a repetition of steps. However, these methods are studied because they are useful for solving certain problems. In thinking through why and how they work, students also deepen their understanding of the properties of the various operations. This work provides opportunities for students to articulate generalizations about the operations and to represent and justify them.

For example, here is one method a third grader might use to solve this problem:

$$\$7.46 + \$3.28 = \$7.50 + \$3.24 = \$10.74$$

The student changed the addition expression to an equivalent expression with numbers that made it easier to find the sum mentally. First graders often use this idea as they learn some of their addition combinations, transforming a combination they are learning into an equivalent combination they already know: $7 + 5 = 6 + 6 = 12$.

When students try to use the same method to make a subtraction problem easier to solve, they find that they must modify their method to create an equivalent problem. Instead of adding an amount to one number and subtracting it from the other, as in addition, they must add the same amount to (or subtract it from) each number:

$$182 - 69 = 183 - 70 = 113$$

Throughout the *Investigations* curriculum, methods like these are introduced and studied to deepen students' understanding of how these operations work and to engage them in proving their ideas using representations of the operations.

Because the ways in which a problem might be changed to make an equivalent problem that is easier to solve can vary (although it might be possible to precisely specify a particular variant of one of these methods), these methods are not algorithms. Students do not generally use such methods to solve a whole class of problems (e.g., any addition problem); rather, students who are flexible in their understanding of numbers and operations use finding equivalent expressions as one possible method and notice when a problem lends itself to solving in this way.

Learning Algorithms Across the Grades

In *Investigations,* students develop, use, and compare algorithms and other methods. These are not "invented" but are constructed with teacher support, as students' understanding of the operations and the base-ten number system grow (see the Teacher Note, Computational Fluency and Place Value). Because the algorithms that students learn are so grounded in knowledge of the operation and the number system, most of them arise naturally as students progress from single-digit to multidigit problems. For example, the adding by place addition algorithm shown earlier naturally grows out of what students are learning about how a number such as 24 is composed of 2 tens and 4 ones. It is part of the teacher's role to make these methods explicit, help students understand and practice them, and support students to gradually use more efficient methods. For example, a second grader who is adding on one number in parts might solve $49 + 34$ by adding on 10, then another 10, then another 10, then 4 to 49 ($49 + 10 + 10 + 10 + 4$). By having this student compare solutions with another student's whose first step is $49 + 30$, the teacher helps the first student analyze what is the same and different about their solutions and opens up the possibility for the first student of a more efficient method—adding on a multiple of 10 all at once rather than breaking it into 10s.

The algorithms and other methods that students learn about and use in *Investigations* for multidigit problems are characterized by their *transparency*. Transparent algorithms

- make the properties of the operations visible.

- show the place value of the numbers in the problem.

- make clear how a problem is broken into subproblems and how the results of these subproblems are recombined.

These characteristics are critical for students while they are learning the meaning of the operations and are building their understanding of the base-ten system. Here is an example of a transparent multiplication algorithm that might be used by a fourth grader:

$$
\begin{array}{r}
34 \\
\times\ 78 \\
\hline
2100 \\
280 \\
240 \\
32 \\
\hline
\end{array}
$$

$$2{,}000 + 500 + 150 + 2 = 2{,}652$$

In this algorithm, students record all numbers fully, showing the place value of all the digits. Because the result of each multiplication is shown, the application of the distributive property is kept track of clearly.

There is a misperception that many different algorithms might arise in a single classroom and that this multitude of algorithms will be confusing. In fact, there are only a few basic algorithms and methods for each operation that arise from students' work and that are emphasized in the curriculum. Each is tied closely to how students solve problems and to the basic characteristics and properties of the operation. Teacher Notes throughout the curriculum provide more detail about these methods.

Students can and do develop efficiency and fluency with these more transparent algorithms. As they do, they do some steps mentally and may no longer need to write out every step to keep track of their work. For example, in using the adding by place algorithm to add $249 + 674$, a competent user might simply jot down 800, 110, 13, and then add those partial sums mentally and record the answer. There may be times when you require students to write out their complete solution method so that you can see how they are solving problems, but for everyday use, efficient users of such algorithms will record only the steps they need.

These algorithms and methods are studied, compared, and analyzed for different reasons. All of them are transparent, preserve place value, and make visible important properties such as distributivity. Some can be practiced and provide general, efficient methods. Others are useful only for particular problems but are studied because of what they illuminate about the operations.

Studying the U.S. Standard Algorithms

The U.S. standard algorithms for addition, subtraction, and multiplication are also explicitly studied in *Investigations* but only after students are fully grounded in understanding the operation and using transparent algorithms for multidigit computation. These algorithms were developed for efficiency and compactness for handwritten computation. When these algorithms are used as a primary teaching tool, their very compactness, which can be an advantage for experienced users, becomes a disadvantage for young learners because they obscure the place value of the numbers and the properties of the operation.

Some students do use the standard algorithms with understanding. As these algorithms come up in class, they should be incorporated into the list of class strategies. Teachers should make sure that students who use them understand what the shortcut notation represents and that they can explain why these algorithms make sense. They should also know and understand other methods. In Grade 4, students revisit the U.S. standard addition algorithm formally, analyze how and why it works, and compare it to other algorithms they are using. In Grade 5, students revisit the U.S. standard subtraction and multiplication algorithms in the same way. Division methods studied in this curriculum focus on the inverse relationship between multiplication and division.

Representations and Contexts for Mathematical Work

Mathematics involves describing and analyzing all kinds of mathematical relationships. Throughout the *Investigations* curriculum, students use representations and contexts to help them visualize these mathematical relationships. Thinking with representations and contexts allows students to express and further develop their ideas and enables students to engage with each other's ideas. Whether solving a multiplication problem, finding the area of a rectangle, describing the relationship between two variables, or ordering fractions, students use representations and contexts to investigate and explain.

The *Investigations* curriculum introduces a limited number of carefully chosen representations and contexts because they provide representations of mathematical relationships that students can use to solve problems and/or to show their ideas and solutions to others. Students may first use representations or contexts concretely, drawing or modeling with materials. Later, they incorporate these representations and contexts into mental models that they can call on to visualize the structure of problems and their solutions. Students develop the habit of making drawings, building models, and using representations to think with and to explain their thinking to others. They develop a repertoire of representations that they know well and can apply when faced with unfamiliar problem situations.

Good contexts and representations have the following characteristics:

- They are useful for a whole class of problems (e.g., addition problems).

- They can be extended to accommodate more complex problems and/or students' expanding repertoire of numbers.

- They do not overwhelm or interfere with the focus on mathematical content.

- Their structure embodies important characteristics of the mathematical relationships.

This Teacher Note provides some examples of how models, materials, and contexts are used by students across the grades.

Representations

Basic representations in the *Investigations* curriculum include connecting cubes, the 100 chart (and its variants, the 300, 1,000, and 10,000 charts), number lines, arrays, and sets of two-dimensional (2-D) and three-dimensional (3-D) shapes. Each representation provides access to certain characteristics, actions, and properties of numbers and operations or of geometric properties and relationships. Here are two examples.

Connecting Cubes

Connecting cubes are a basic material for counting and for modeling addition and subtraction in Grades K–2. The cubes are a discrete model of whole numbers and provide a uniform counting material for representing ones. Because they connect, they can be organized into sticks of ten cubes so that students can use them to represent tens and ones.

The individual cubes are visible in the connected stick of ten, so students can visualize how this stick represents the equivalence of 1 ten and 10 ones and then how 10 ten-sticks is equivalent to 1 hundred and 100 ones. Connecting cubes are a flexible material. They are well suited for modeling the basic actions of joining and separating. They can also be used to construct rectangular arrays for studying multiplication and area. Students also use the cubes to construct rectangular prisms and to analyze and visualize how the volume of the shape consists of a certain number of layers, each of which has the same dimensions.

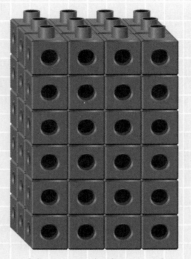

Each layer is 3 × 4. There are six layers.

The Number Line

The number line is another key representation of numbers. This continuous representation offers students another view of the number sequence and number relationships. Students' beginning work with number lines involves number lines that are already marked with the counting numbers.

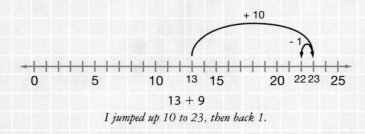

13 + 9
I jumped up 10 to 23, then back 1.

Later, students choose the part of the number line they need and which points on it should be marked as they use it to solve problems.

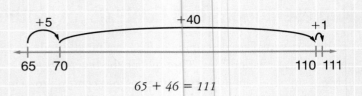

65 + 46 = 111

The number line provides access to the idea that numbers are infinite. At first, students come to this idea in relation to the counting sequence of whole numbers. Later, as they encounter negative numbers, they consider how the number line extends in both directions, that both positive and negative numbers "go on forever." In their study of rational numbers, they use the number line to model fractions and decimal fractions and consider how the segments of the number line between two successive whole numbers can be divided into smaller and smaller pieces. In later years, they will come to understand that there are an infinite number of numbers between any two successive integers.

For students to use a representation well, they need enough experience with it so that they understand its basic characteristics and can then use it themselves to model and solve problems. For example, using an unmarked number line flexibly requires that students have enough prior experience using the marked number line to count, add, and subtract.

Using Different Representations

Different representations offer different models of the mathematics and access to different mathematical ideas. For example, both place value models and number lines are useful in students' study of subtraction, but they each allow students to see different aspects of subtraction. A student solving the problem 103 − 37 might think about subtracting 37 in parts by visualizing a place value model of the numbers, subtracting 3 tens and then 7 ones (which, for ease of subtraction from 103, the student might split into 3 + 4).

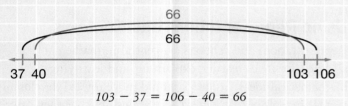

Another student might think about creating an easier, equivalent problem: $103 - 37 = 106 - 40$. This student might visualize "sliding" the interval from 37 to 103 along a number line to determine how to change the numbers, while preserving the difference between them.

$$103 - 37 = 106 - 40 = 66$$

More details about these and other representations are provided throughout the curriculum units.

Contexts

Contexts and stories are also used to represent mathematical relationships. A good context can be created from familiar events or fantasy. Contexts that students can imagine and visualize give them access to ways of thinking about the mathematical ideas and relationships they are studying. For a context to be useful, it must be connected enough to students' experience that students can imagine and represent the actions and relationships. At the same time, the details of the context need not be elaborate, so that the nonmathematical aspects of the context stay in the background. Here are two examples.

The Penny Jar

One of the contexts in the patterns and functions units in Grades 1 and 4 is the Penny Jar. The Penny Jar contains some number of pennies (the starting amount) and then has a certain number of pennies added to it each day or with each round (the constant rate of change). This is one of the contexts used to engage students in exploring a function—the relationship of the number of days to the total number of pennies—that involves a constant rate of change. Students' knowledge of similar real-world contexts engages students quickly in the mathematics and helps them visualize the mathematical relationships, but it is not so elaborate that it obscures or distracts from the mathematics.

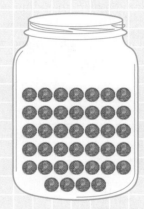

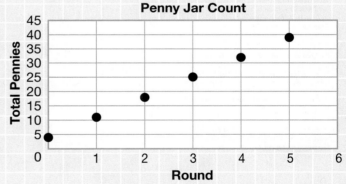

Number of Rounds	Total Number of Pennies
Start	4
1	11
2	18
3	25
4	32
5	39

Once students are familiar with the Penny Jar context, they can represent it in multiple ways, using pictures, tables, and graphs, to describe and analyze the relationship between the two variables.

Travel Stories

In Grade 3, travel stories are used as a context for subtraction. Students are familiar with taking trips by car or bus or have encountered such trips in stories or movies. They know about a trip having a starting point, an ending point, and a certain distance traveled. They are also familiar with stopping along the way for a meal or to take a break and with discussing how much of the distance has been covered and how much is still ahead of them.

Name _____ Date _____

Collections and Travel Stories

More Travel Problems

Write an equation to represent each problem.
Then solve each one and show your solutions.

1. Last weekend, the McDonald family took the train to Center City. The train traveled 16 miles before stopping at the White Pines station to pick up more passengers. When the train pulled into the Center City station, it had traveled 93 miles in all. How far did the train travel from the White Pines station to Center City?

2. The Chan family visited their cousins last summer. They set the trip meter on their car at 0 before they left home. They stopped at a rest area 42 miles from their home. Later, they stopped to get lunch at a restaurant 100 miles from their home. How far did they travel from the rest area to the restaurant?

3. When the Chan family arrived at their cousins' house, the trip meter read 138 miles. How far did they travel from the rest area to their cousins' house?

58　Unit 3　　　　　　　　　　　　　　　　Session 3.5

© Pearson Education 3

▲ **Grade 3 Unit 3** *Student Activity Book*, **page 58**

Helping Students Connect to Contexts

Teachers often personalize these contexts for students to help them visualize and use it. For example, when using the Penny Jar context, one first-grade teacher had a brief discussion about places they or someone else they know used

to hold money and some reasons that money might get added to any of these. The teacher then referred to some of these situations as they discussed problems, "Let's say we're talking about Andre's situation when he is doing his chores. He has 3 pennies in the jar, and he is going to put in 2 pennies for each chore he completes." In using the travel story context, teachers also refer to situations that are familiar to students: "So let's say Janelle and her family are setting off to visit her grandma, like they did last summer, and the whole trip is 274 miles. ..."

More details about these and other contexts are provided throughout the curriculum units.

Using Representations and Contexts

Representations and contexts are central in mathematics at all levels for investigating, explaining, and justifying mathematical ideas. Students should move toward developing mental models of mathematical relationships that they call on routinely and will often use pictures, diagrams, and objects when they encounter new kinds of problems.

Students should use representations and contexts judiciously and with purpose. A first grader who is solving word problems that involve addition and subtraction might model every problem with cubes. Another student in the same class might model one or two problems; then, having visually confirmed the action of the operation, the student might solve the rest by imagining one quantity and counting on. A third student—or the same student later in the year—might reason about the numbers without using an image or model. In class discussions, both the teacher and students use representations to clarify and investigate mathematical ideas and to help all students focus on what is being discussed.

As a teacher, one of your roles is to support students in using representations and contexts and to help them develop mental images that they can call on. On the one hand, students need not show a picture for a problem when they have developed more efficient numerical tools and methods. For example, when one fourth grader was asked to solve a multiplication problem in two ways, he solved the problem by breaking it up efficiently, using the distributive property, and then showed a solution using groups of tally marks. His teacher let him know that using tally marks was not what she was looking for from him and reminded him of the work the class had been doing on changing one of the numbers in the problem and then adjusting the product.

On the other hand, students should understand that the use of representations and models is not a "crutch" in mathematics but is a powerful set of tools for investigating problem situations. In the classroom, encourage representation as a central part of mathematics activity. Make a habit of asking questions such as these:

- Is there a way you can show us your thinking using the number line or the 100 chart?

- Can you explain how your strategy makes sense using the travel context we have been using for some of the problems?

- You used a number line and Chris used a place-value sketch showing tens and ones. What is similar or different about these two approaches? Where can you see the four tens in Chris's place value sketch on Luc's number line solution?

- Karen, you are thinking of the multiplication problem as representing 47 classrooms with 23 students in each class. How did this context help you keep track of the parts of the problem?

- Can you show us with a picture or on the Geoboard what you mean when you say "a triangle is half of a rectangle"?

- What if you needed to explain or prove what you are saying to someone who came to visit our classroom? Is there a way you can show me why what you are saying is true with a picture or diagram?

When students are accustomed to incorporating representations in their daily mathematics work and considering what representations can be helpful for explaining mathematical ideas, they can also create their own images appropriate to a particular problem situation. Help students make these images simple enough so that they serve the mathematics rather than obscure it. The use of representations in class discussions helps illuminate students' ideas for each other and, by putting out an image that is available to all students, clarifies what mathematical relationships are being considered and invites more students into the conversation.

For further examples of students' use of representations, see the classroom stories in the section "Language and Representation" in Part 7, Working with the Range of Learners: Classroom Cases.

Foundations of Algebra in the Elementary Grades

Algebra is a multifaceted area of mathematics content that has been described and classified in different ways. Across many of the classification schemes, four areas foundational to the study of algebra stand out: (1) generalizing and formalizing patterns; (2) representing and analyzing the structure of numbers and operations; (3) using symbolic notation to express functions and relations; and (4) representing and analyzing change.

In the *Investigations* curriculum, these areas of early algebra are addressed in two major ways: (1) work within the counting, number, and operations units focusing on generalizations that arise in the course of students' study of numbers and operations and (2) a coherent strand, consisting of one unit in each grade, K–5, that focuses on patterns, functions, and change. These two areas of emphasis are described here, followed by some additional information about the goals of work on early algebra in the curriculum.

Early Algebra: Making General Claims About Numbers and Operations

Each *Investigations* unit on counting, numbers, and operations includes a focus on reasoning and generalizing about numbers and operations. Even in beginning work with numbers and operations in Kindergarten and Grade 1, students are already noticing regularities about numbers and operations. For example, in the K–1 game *Double Compare,* each student in the pair selects two number cards. The student with the greater sum says "me." In this early work, before students know their single-digit addition combinations, most students are counting all or counting on to determine the sum. But consider how students are reasoning in the following brief episode:

> Bridget and Siva are playing *Double Compare.* Bridget draws a 5 and a 2; Siva draws a 5 and a 3 and immediately says "me," indicating that he has the

greater sum. Siva usually counts both amounts by ones to get the sum, so the teacher asks him, "How did you know you have more?" Siva responds, "Because I have a 3 and she has a 2, and 3 is bigger." Bridget is nodding vigorously and adds, "The 5s don't count."

How are the students in this episode figuring out who has the greater sum? Why does Siva only compare 3 with 2, and what does Bridget mean when she says the "5s don't count"? Implicit in these students' work is a general claim about adding numbers that many young students use: If you are comparing two addition expressions, and one of the addends in the first expression is the same as one of the addends in the second, then you need only compare the other two addends to determine which expression has the greater sum. This is a mouthful to put into words, and students might not be able to articulate this idea completely; nevertheless, they are reasoning based on this idea. In later years, this idea can be represented with symbolic notation:

For any numbers a, b, c, and d when $a = c$ and $b < d$, then $a + b < c + d$.

$a = c$	$b < d$	$a + b < c + d$
$5 = 5$	$2 < 3$	$5 + 2 < 5 + 3$

Part of the teaching work in the elementary grades is to help students articulate, represent, investigate, and justify such general claims that arise naturally in the course of their work with numbers and operations. In each of the number and operations units in Grades K–5, the Algebra Connections essay highlights several of these general ideas about properties and relationships relevant to the work in that curriculum unit, with examples of how students think about and represent them. Investigation and discussion of some of these generalizations are built into unit sessions; for others, Algebra Notes alert the teacher to activities or discussions in which these ideas are likely to arise and could be pursued.

In the course of articulating, representing, and justifying their ideas about such general claims, students in the elementary grades are beginning to engage in proving—a central part of mathematics. They consider the questions: Does this generalization apply to *all* numbers (in the domain under consideration, usually whole numbers)? Why does it work? How do you know? In two of the number and operations units in each grade, 2–5, you will find a Teacher Note that focuses on proof and justification. These Teacher Notes provide examples of the ways that students at that grade level engage in proving and how their proofs, based on representations, are related to the proofs a mathematician might carry out.

Examples of the general claims highlighted in the curriculum in Grades K–2 are as follows:

- Counting the same set of objects in different orders results in the same count.

- If one number is larger than another, and the same number is added to each, the first total will be larger than the second: $3 + 5 > 2 + 5$.

- You can add two numbers in either order: $6 + 3 = 3 + 6$.

- If you add an amount to one addend and subtract it from another addend, the sum remains the same: $6 + 6 = 12$; $7 + 5 = 12$.

- Addition and subtraction are related. If adding two numbers gives a certain sum, then subtracting one of the addends from the sum results in the other addend: $6 + 7 = 13$; $13 - 7 = 6$; $13 - 6 = 7$.

- You can break numbers into parts to add them: $6 + 8 = 6 + (4 + 4) = (6 + 4) + 4$.

- If you add two even numbers, the sum is even. If you add two odd numbers, the sum is even. If you add an even number and an odd number, the sum is odd.

Some of the generalizations investigated in Grades K–2 are revisited in Grades 3–5 with higher numbers and more complex problems. In addition, new general claims are investigated. Examples of general claims highlighted in Grades 3–5 are as follows:

- If you add the same amount to both numbers in a subtraction problem, the difference does not change: $145 - 97 = 148 - 100$.

- You can multiply two numbers in either order: $32 \times 20 = 20 \times 32$.

- You can break numbers into parts to multiply them, but each part of each number must be multiplied by each part of the other number: $7 \times 24 = 7 \times (20 + 4) = (7 \times 20) + (7 \times 4)$.

- Multiplication and division are related. If multiplying two numbers gives a certain product, then dividing that product by one of the original factors results in the other factor: $9 \times 8 = 72$; $72 \div 8 = 9$; $72 \div 9 = 8$.

- A factor of a number is a factor of multiples of that number: 3 is a factor of 15; 15 is a factor of 30, so 3 is a factor of 30.

- If you double (or triple) one of the factors in a multiplication problem and halve (or third) the other, the product remains the same: $164 \times 4 = 328 \times 2$.

Early Algebra: Patterns, Functions, and Change

Investigations includes a coherent K–5 strand on patterns, functions, and change, with one unit in each grade. The content of these units starts with repeating patterns and number sequences in Grades K and 1, connects these patterns and sequences to functional relationships beginning in Grade 2, and then develops ideas about linear and nonlinear contexts that involve relationships between two variables in Grades 3–5. In each of these units in K–5, the Algebra Connections essay highlights some of the ideas students work on in that unit, and how they connect to later work in algebra.

Patterns and Functions in Grades K–2

Work with repeating patterns has long been a staple of mathematics work in the primary grades, but it often seems to have little connection to work in later grades. In the *Investigations* sequence, students' study of the structure of repeating patterns is connected to work with ratios and linear functions by associating the repeating pattern with the counting numbers. Consider this example:

Students have been building repeating color patterns using connecting cubes. This red-blue-green repeating pattern has been numbered with the counting numbers, starting with 1. Students are considering which numbers are associated with the green cubes:

1 2 3 4 5 6 7 8 9 10 11 12

Kamala says that the greens have a "counting by 3s" pattern: 3, 6, 9, 12. Esperanza says, "it will always be on the threes because every time you skip two, then it's green." Theo adds, remembering a previous Investigation in which they built buildings from connecting cubes with the same number of cubes in each layer: "It's like the same pattern we made when we made the building. It's always adding threes. One floor is three, two floors is six, and you keep adding three— 3, 6, 9, um, 12, and you keep going by 3s."

Students are recognizing the underlying 1:3 ratio in both situations. In the repeating pattern, there is a relationship between the position of each green cube among all green cubes and its position among all the cubes: the *first* green is in position 3 in the sequence, the *second* green in position 6, the *third* green in position 9, and so forth. In the cube building, there are 3 cubes for each floor: one floor has

3 cubes, 2 floors have 6 cubes, 3 floors have 9 cubes, and so forth. These constant ratio situations are students' first examples of linear change—change at a constant rate.

Examples of ideas investigated in Grades K–2 in these units are as follows:

- Repeating patterns can be described as iterations of a unit. This repeating color pattern can be divided into its units, the part that repeats:

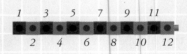

- When the elements of a repeating pattern are numbered with the counting numbers, elements in the pattern can be characterized by a particular number sequence. In a red-blue-red-blue connecting cube train, the blue cubes are numbered 2, 4, 6, 8, . . . , and the red cubes are numbered 1, 3, 5, 7, ...

     1   3   5   7   9   11
      2   4   6   8   10   12

- The same number sequence can represent different situations. The blue cubes in a red-blue repeating pattern and the claps in a tap-clap repeating pattern fall in the same numbered positions.

- In a ratio situation, as one quantity changes by a certain amount, the other quantity always changes by a certain amount (for each day, there are 3 pennies added to the jar).

- Tables are a representation that can be used to show how one variable changes in relation to another.

- The same ratio relationship can occur in different contexts (e.g., 3 pennies per day, 3 cubes per "floor").

Patterns, Functions, and Change in Grades 3–5

In Grades 3–5, students focus on both linear and nonlinear change. Students study situations with a constant rate of change, in which two variables are related in ways that can be expressed in a verbal rule or an equation (such as the relationship between the total number of pennies in a jar and the number of days pennies have been collected, when a fixed number of pennies is added to the jar each day). They learn to take into account any starting amount (i.e., the number of pennies in the jar at the beginning) and the rate of change (i.e., the number of pennies added to the jar each day). They also study relationships in which the value of one variable cannot be determined based on the value of the other (such as the relationship between temperature and time in Grade 3 and between plant growth and time in Grade 4). In Grades 4 and 5, they also encounter situations in which the relationship between the two variables can be determined, but the change is not occurring at a constant rate, for example, a Penny Jar in which the number of pennies doubles each day.

Students work extensively with ways of representing relationships between two variables: with words, with tables and graphs, with numbers, and (starting in Grade 4) with symbolic notation. These units reinforce and connect with work in other units on multiplication, ratio, area, volume, and graphing. The Algebra Connections essay in each of the patterns, functions, and change units provides more detailed information about this sequence of students' work and how it connects to algebra.

Examples of ideas investigated in these units in Grades 3–5 (in addition to some of those in the K–2 list that continue to be studied in new contexts) are as follows:

- Line graphs are a representation that can show the relationship between two variables. A line graph represents both individual values of the variable and the rate of change of one variable in relation to another.

- In a situation with a constant rate of change, the value of one variable can be determined, given the value of the other.

- The relationship between two variables in a situation with a constant rate of change can be described in words and with symbolic notation.

- In some situations, the rate of change is determined but not constant. In these situations, the rate of change may be, for example, increasing by a constant amount.

Early Algebra Is Fundamental

Underlying the work in early algebra are, according to one of the *Investigations'* mathematician advisors, "foundational principles"—principles that connect elementary students' work in arithmetic to later work in algebra. For example, when second graders consider how changing the order of numbers in an addition or subtraction problem affects the sum or difference, they can engage in reasoning about foundational ideas, in this case, that addition is commutative, but subtraction is not: $a + b = b + a$, but $c - d \neq d - c$. Even though they may not yet have the experience with negative numbers to allow them to completely make sense of $14 - 26$, they see, through modeling and representing this problem, that it does not have the same difference as $26 - 14$. In later years, they will come to see that there *is* a regularity here, that if $c - d = a$, then $d - c = -a$, or $c - d = -(d - c)$.

Similarly, when fifth graders develop representations to show why halving one factor in a multiplication problem and doubling the other results in the same product, they are applying knowledge of foundational properties of multiplication and division. In later years, they may explain the more general claim that dividing one factor by any number (except 0) and multiplying the other factor by the same number maintains the same product by reference to the associative property of multiplication and to multiplication by 1—the identity element for multiplication. Through a series of steps, based on these properties of multiplication, one can show that, if a, b, and n are numbers $(n \neq 0)$, then $a \times b = a \times b \times \frac{n}{n} = (a \times n) \times \left(\frac{b}{n}\right)$.

For most adults, notation such as the use of variables, operations, and equal signs is the chief identifying feature of algebra. Although students use symbolic notation in Grades 4 and 5, the notation is not the focus of activity in Grades K–5. Underlying the notation are ways of reasoning about how the operations work. This *reasoning* about how numbers can be put together and taken apart under different operations or about relationships between two changing quantities, *not* the notation, is the central work of elementary students in algebra.

Algebra for All Students

Work in early algebra in the elementary classroom has the potential of enhancing the learning of *all* students. The teachers with whom the *Investigations* team collaborated during the development of the curriculum commented on this potential in their classrooms. Teacher collaborators reported that students who tend to have difficulty in mathematics become stronger mathematical thinkers through this work. As one teacher wrote, "When I began to work on generalizations with my students, I noticed a shift in my less capable learners. Things seemed more accessible to them." When the generalizations are made explicit—through language and representations used to justify them—they become accessible to more students and can become the foundation for greater computational fluency. Furthermore, the disposition to create a representation when a mathematical question arises supports students in reasoning through their confusions.

At the same time, students who generally outperform their peers in mathematics find this content challenging and stimulating. The study of numbers and operations extends beyond efficient computation to the excitement of making and proving conjectures about mathematical relationships that apply to an infinite class of numbers. A teacher explained, "Students develop a habit of mind of looking beyond the activity to search for something more, some broader mathematical context to fit the experience into."

Early algebra is not an add-on. The foundations of algebra arise naturally throughout students' work with numbers, operations, and patterns and by using familiar and accessible contexts to investigate how one set of values changes in relation to another. This work anchors students' concepts of the operations and underlies greater computational flexibility.

Discussing Mathematical Ideas

Throughout the *Investigations* curriculum, whole-class discussion is a key aspect of students' mathematical activity. Class discussion provides a time for students to

- articulate their mathematical ideas.

- share different approaches to solving a problem.

- identify and investigate what they don't understand.

- analyze why a solution works or how it is flawed.

- pose conjectures and identify evidence to support them.

- collaborate to build ideas or solve problems.

- develop mathematical language.

- use representations to describe mathematical relationships.

- compare and connect students' various ideas, representations, and solutions.

- learn to consider and question each other's ideas.

By carefully selecting problems, representations, and solutions for the whole class to consider, the teacher focuses discussion on key mathematical ideas and works with the class as a whole to move students' thinking forward.

Building a Mathematical Community

In the first weeks of school, teachers help the class develop norms for classroom discussion and work with students on attitudes and behavior that will support productive math discussions. Most teachers find that they need to work quite explicitly with students throughout the school year to first establish and then maintain expectations for class discussion. During discussions, teachers keep the flow of ideas organized and remind students about the appropriate focus. For example, "Right now I want comments that are either agreeing with, disagreeing with, or commenting on Yolanda's idea," or "So we now have three different approaches to this problem on the board. Is there a way in which Jill's is similar to Corey's?" Teachers also find opportunities to comment directly on student actions, behavior, and contributions that support productive discourse:

> Because Stephen was willing to talk through what was confusing him when he got an answer that he knew wasn't right, it seemed to really help all of us understand this kind of problem better.

> When Kamala put up her picture of the problem, I heard some of you say, "Ooh!" What was it you understood when you saw that picture? Did anyone else have a picture or a diagram that helped you understand how to solve this problem?

And from time to time teachers discuss directly with the class what aspects of class discussions have been helping or hindering students' participation:

> What helps you be willing to share your work or make an observation during class discussion? Are there times you don't feel comfortable speaking? Why is that?

Building an inclusive mathematics classroom involves a focus on respect for student ideas and acceptance of differences. Working on establishing this community with students will vary across grades and even from one year to another, depending on the needs and experiences of your students. (See the section "Setting Up the Mathematical Community" in Part 7, Working with the Range of Learners: Classroom Cases for some teachers' thoughts on building the classroom mathematics community.)

Focusing Class Discussions

Students' ideas are important and are, in fact, central to discussion. But if a discussion bounces among too many different ideas or tries to include too many different approaches, the discussion becomes ungrounded and hard for students to follow. Simply listing one problem-solving approach after another doesn't engage students beyond the few moments when they are contributing their own idea.

The Math Focus Points for Discussion and sample teacher dialogue found in the text for every discussion will help you guide the discussion. In preparing for class, ask yourself:

- What do I want this discussion to accomplish?

- What do I want all students to take away from this discussion?

- How will the time spent as a whole class enhance the work students have done individually or in pairs or groups?

During work that precedes the discussion, observe students' work with the upcoming discussion in mind. Ask yourself:

- What is a difficulty that many students are having?

- What is a problem that many students are struggling with?

- Is there a question that one pair or group came up with that it would be fruitful for the whole class to discuss?

- What are the basic approaches to solving this problem that students are using?

- Which students or groups have ideas or approaches that should be shared?

Student Participation

Whole-class discussion time is precious class time; it should serve to consolidate or move ahead the math thinking of all students. Find ways during discussions to elicit responses from different students. Although all students may not participate in any one discussion, all of your students' voices should be heard over the course of several discussions. There are many ways to work with students to encourage them to participate. For example, listen carefully to students' ideas and look carefully at their work during activities. Help particular students prepare to share one of their ideas. At first, some students might be more comfortable if you put their solution, representation, or idea on the board or a

transparency and present it to the class yourself; alternatively, the student might explain a certain part of the solution, while you add to the student's explanation.

Think of ways to invite all students' participation during each discussion by asking students to raise hands if they used the same approach or if they agree or disagree with a statement you or another student makes. Pose a question and have students discuss it for a few minutes in pairs before having the whole class consider it. Use wait time judiciously and think about ways that students can use quiet signals when they are ready to respond (e.g., thumbs up rather than hands waving); then students who are still thinking are not distracted.

Ideas are bound to come up that you cannot pursue during class discussions. Sometimes you cannot follow or decipher a student's idea at the moment or you are not sure about how it relates to what is being discussed. If you don't understand what a student is saying, you might ask another student to interpret or talk to the student later. Don't be afraid to let students know that you have to think about something and get back to them or follow up with them after the discussion. You can always bring an idea back to the class later if you decide it would be important for the class to think about it.

You can find other ways to follow up on a student's idea that is not central or accessible for the whole class: "I was thinking about your idea, and here's a problem I thought you could try it on." Some teachers have a "parking lot" poster for ideas that come up during class but they don't have time to pursue. These ideas may come up again later or can be referred to when they become relevant. The better you know the curriculum, the more you will know when they might come up.

Setting Up the Classroom for Discussion

It is critical that students are sitting in such a way that everyone is focused on the discussion and everyone can hear. If there are representations that students need to see during the discussions, they must be large enough and dark enough so that everyone can see them.

A variety of seating arrangements for class discussions can work, as long as there are clear expectations connected to them. In some classrooms, students gather on a rug for the class meeting and then return to their places or choose places for work time. In other classrooms, students often stay at their own desks for meetings. Some teachers vary the setting, with students staying at their desks when the meeting will be short and gathering together when a longer time is needed.

To facilitate a smooth transition to meeting on the rug, some teachers assign students places to sit on the rug, changing them every month or so. Others place circles, mats, or white boards to clearly mark the places available for students to sit. Others allow students to sit wherever they want in a circle as long as they can see the teacher and all of the other students. They might remind students to make a good choice about sitting in a position and next to classmates that enables them to focus on the discussion. While some students can pay attention while sitting on the floor, others do better in a chair.

Guidelines for Whole-Class Discussions

In summary, here are some guidelines to keep in mind for your class's whole-group discussions:

- Set up norms and review them frequently; point out examples in which they are working.

- Plan a clear purpose and focus for each discussion, based on the listed Focus Points.

- Use wait time to give students time to think.

- Ask students to use quiet student signals to indicate they are ready to respond.

- Prepare with some students ahead of time to participate in the discussion.

- Have clear visuals that everyone can see and refer to.

- Establish a routine arrangement that ensures that everyone can hear and see.

- Select only a few students to share solutions.

When all students come to a discussion prepared to listen actively and to contribute ideas, the class discussions provide an important forum in which they can articulate, represent, connect, and consolidate the mathematical ideas they have been working on.

Racial and Linguistic Diversity in the Classroom:
What Does Equity Mean in Today's Math Classroom?

… we have no patterns for relating across our human differences as equals. As a result, those differences have been misnamed and misused in the service of separation and confusion.[1]

Audre Lorde

We must not, in trying to think about how we can make a big difference, ignore the small daily differences we can make, which, over time, add up to big differences that we often cannot foresee.[2]

Marian Wright Edelman

U.S. public schools are responsible for educating students who are more racially and linguistically diverse than at any other time in our history. The beginning of the 21st century in the United States is marked by an influx of immigrants, and schools and teachers are at the front door meeting these students. Hence, many teachers work in classrooms with increasing numbers of immigrant students, students of color, and linguistically diverse students who often face unique challenges related to language proficiency, cultural and social adaptation, and poverty. What are the issues and challenges for teachers in these diverse classrooms?

While developing this curriculum, the *Investigations* staff and field-test teachers worked together to continue educating ourselves about this question. Many of us have had direct experience teaching in schools where students come from diverse racial, cultural, and linguistic backgrounds. In many cases, the students' culture, race, ethnicity, and first language are different from those of the teacher. This Teacher Note provides a glimpse into the complex issues about racial, cultural, and linguistic diversity being discussed in the field of education today. It also provides resources for further reading, including those we found helpful in our own professional development.

Equity in the Mathematics Classroom

Equity does not mean that every student should receive identical instruction; instead, it demands that reasonable and appropriate accommodations be made as needed to promote access and attainment for all students. (NCTM, 2000, p. 11)

Investigations was developed with the assumption that all learners can engage in challenging and substantive mathematics. Assumptions about students' capacity and inclination to learn in school can undermine their access to and participation in significant mathematics learning. An extensive body of literature documents the persistence of these assumptions and their effects on students' opportunity to learn. For example, students of color and those whose first language is not English are often seen in terms of what they lack instead of what they bring to the learning environment (termed in the literature a *deficit thinking* model). Student underperformance in school may be explained by student and family shortcomings, behavior that does not match a particular set of norms, immaturity, or lack of intelligence. Students who do not speak fluent English may be judged as having poor or underdeveloped conceptual understanding because they cannot yet express the complexity of their thinking in English. Misunderstanding cultural differences can lead schools to inappropriately place children into special education and low-ability groups and to expect less from them than from other children. For instance, Entwistle and Alexander (1989) report that poor black children are often described as less mature, and, consequently, school personnel may hold lower expectations for them than for children whose socioeconomic status is higher.

---

[1] From a paper delivered at the Copeland Colloquium, Amherst College, in April, 1980. The paper was entitled, "Age, Race, Class, and Sex: Women Redefining Difference."

[2] Marian Wright Edelman, "Families in Peril: An Agenda for Social Change," The W. E. B. Du Bois Lectures (Cambridge, Mass.: Harvard University Press, 1987), p. 107.

Many teachers are working hard to improve learning opportunities for these students, with the goal of enhancing both the learning climate and students' educational performance. In this work, teachers must consider the broader issues as well as practices, procedures, strategies, and other key aspects of schooling. In an educational setting, equity indicates a state in which all children—students of color and white students, males and females, successful students and those who have fallen behind, and students who have been denied access in the past—have equal opportunities to learn, participate in challenging programs, and have equal access to the services they need to benefit from that education. Equity has sometimes been oversimplified to mean that all students should be treated the same—neutrally and without differentiation. Rather, differences matter, and matter in specific ways. Successful learning experiences depend on teachers building on the contributions of all students and recognizing the differences that matter to them.

In the mathematics education literature, researchers from four projects, three in the United States and one in South Africa, looked across their projects to identify features of classrooms "essential for supporting students' understanding" in mathematics (Hiebert et al., 1997). They organize these in five dimensions, one of which is "equity and accessibility." The authors describe this dimension as fundamental:

> [E]quity . . . is not an add-on or an optional dimension. It is an integral part of a system of instruction that sets students' understanding of mathematics as the goal. Without equity, the other dimensions are restricted and the system does not function well. (p. 12)

Race and Linguistic Diversity

While teaching a seminar on race in education several years ago, one of the authors of this essay was met with a remarkable silence and little open discussion of race, racism, and the ways they come up in classroom teaching. Some think that racism is no longer an issue in schools, and that "color blindness" is the way to approach a diverse class of students. However, many in the field believe that explicit classroom attention to race, ethnicity, and home language results in increased communication and learning.

Race (or ethnicity) can have overlapping and coexisting categories of meaning. Sometimes, race signifies being economically, socially, politically, and educationally oppressed. Other times it signifies a sense of community and belonging, involving valuable associations with a particular group, history, cultural codes, and sensibilities. Race conveys multiple meanings, and racism takes on multiple forms, subject to context and situation. Whether expressed subtly or with crude directness, the effects of racism are felt in everyday school experience. Preconceptions about who students are, which are based on surface behaviors, can mask important potential.

For example, in one classroom, a Hmong girl is quiet, well behaved, and does little to demand attention. But although she is well behaved, she is not engaged and does not quite know what's going on in the lesson. In another classroom, a young black boy is distracted and disruptive, eager to contribute, but often "in trouble." The Hmong girl might be seen as a model student—quiet, hard working, high achieving, and nonchallenging of classroom norms. In contrast, the black boy might be seen as loud, threatening, noncompliant, dysfunctional, and low achieving. The characterization of the Hmong girl seems positive, even flattering, in comparison to the characterization of the black boy. However, both views may be silencing the voices, needs, and potential contributions of these children in different ways. For the Hmong girl, a focus on seemingly compliant behavior may lead the teacher to ignore her educational needs. For the black boy, a focus on seemingly bad behavior may distract the teacher from recognizing his educational strengths.

To understand all students' experiences—to support them in rigorous learning and to respect the variety of their language practices, histories, and identities—educators must continue to learn about the issues of race and racism, cultural and linguistic diversity, and teaching practices and strategies that support the learning of all students.

Teaching Practices and Strategies

Many important insights about teaching practices and strategies that support students of color and English language learners can be gleaned from those who have been studying and writing in the field. Some of these educators and researchers focus specifically on the mathematics classroom, but there are also accounts from science and literacy that have a great deal to offer the teaching of mathematics.

Gloria Ladson-Billings studied exemplary teachers of African-American students and has written about an approach of "culturally relevant teaching." Although the teachers she studied differed in the way they structured their classrooms—some appeared more "traditional," while others were more "progressive" in their teaching strategies—their conceptions of and beliefs about teaching and learning had many commonalities. Here is a subset of characteristics of these teachers adapted from Ladson-Billings' list (1995). These teachers:

- believed that all students are capable of academic success.

- saw their pedagogy as always in process.

- developed a community of learners.

- encouraged students to learn collaboratively and be responsible for each other.

- believed that knowledge is shared, recycled, and constructed.

- believed they themselves must be passionate about learning.

- believed they must scaffold, or build bridges, to facilitate learning.

- believed assessment must be multifaceted.

Overall, these teachers supported their students and held them to high standards:

> Students were not permitted to choose failure in their classrooms. They cajoled, nagged, pestered, and bribed

the students to work at high intellectual levels. Absent from their discourse was the "language of lacking." . . . Instead, teachers talked about their own shortcomings and limitations and ways they needed to change to ensure student success. (p. 479)

Critical to teaching students who bring a variety of cultural, social, and linguistic experience into the classroom is what Marilyn Cochran-Smith (1995b) calls "understanding children's understanding":

> [C]entral to learning to teach in a culturally and linguistically diverse society is understanding children's understanding or exploring what it means to know a child, to consider his or her background, behaviors, and interactions with others, and to try to do what Duckworth calls "give reason" to the ways the child constructs meanings and interpretations, drawing on experiences and knowledge developed both inside and outside the classroom. (p. 511)

Eleanor Duckworth, whom Cochran-Smith cites above, may have originated the phrase *understanding children's understanding* in her essay of the same name (1996). In that essay, she discusses the idea of "giving children reason" as she describes a group of teachers in a study group who set themselves this challenge: "[E]very time a child did or said something whose meaning was not immediately obvious . . . [they] sought to understand the way in which . . . [it] could be construed to make sense" (pp. 86–87).

This work of hearing and understanding students' ideas, discourse, and representations and involving all of them in significant intellectual work can be especially challenging when students come from backgrounds quite different from the teacher's own. Cindy Ballenger's *Teaching Other People's Children* (1999) and Vivian Paley's *White Teacher* (1989) provide first-person accounts of teachers who are actively examining their own preconceptions about the behavior and discourse of the students they teach. Ballenger expresses how her initial belief that all students could learn was not enough:

I began with these children expecting deficits, not because I believed they or their background was deficient—I was definitely against such a view—but because I did not know how to see their strengths . . . I came to see . . . strengths . . . that are part of an intellectual tradition, not always a schooled tradition, but an intellectual one nonetheless, and one that, therefore, had a great deal to say to teaching and learning. (p. 3)

Ballenger recounts her journey in learning to listen to the sense of her students, both "honoring the child's home discourse" and engaging the student in "school-based and discipline-based ways of talking, acting, and knowing" (p. 6).

Working in English with students whose first language is not English presents two challenges to teachers who do not share the student's first language: (1) how to learn about, respect, and support the discourse practices that students can contribute from their own knowledge and communities; and (2) how to bring students into the language of the discipline of mathematics in English. Judit Moschkovich (1999) identifies two critical functions of mathematical discussions for English language learners: "uncovering the mathematical content in student contributions and bringing different ways of talking and points of view into contact" (p. 11). She identifies several important instructional strategies that support these students' participation in math discussions (p. 11):

- using several expressions for the same concept

- using gestures and objects to clarify meaning

- accepting and building on student responses

- revoicing student statements with more technical terms

- focusing not only on vocabulary development but also on mathematical content and argumentation practices

Josiane Hudicourt-Barnes (2003) writes about the participation of students whose home language is Haitian Creole. Her research highlights the way that understanding the forms of discourse students contribute from their own culture enables teachers to uncover and appreciate how students are making sense of subject matter. Although she writes about science learning, her observations are applicable to the mathematics classroom: "To be 'responsive to the children and responsible to the subject matter' (Ball, 1997, p. 776), we must be able to hear children's diverse voices and create opportunities for them to pursue their ideas and questions (p. 17)." Further, she argues that classroom discourse that follows a rigid, restrictive format "may mean that children from families of non-Western traditions are shut out of classroom participation and that skills from other traditions are devalued and subtracted from children's cognitive repertoires, and therefore also made unavailable to their fellow students" (p. 17).

Being "responsive to the children and responsive to the subject matter" is highlighted by many of the writers in this field. They emphasize that the teacher's responsibility is *both* to the students' ideas, sense making, and forms of discourse *and* to bringing these students in to the ideas, vocabulary, and ways of working in the discipline of the content area. Gloria Ladson-Billings (2002) sums up her observations of a teacher whose urban, largely African American, students, initially hated writing:

To meet the academic goals he had set, Carter had to rethink his practice in some fundamental ways. . . . He had to keep a sense of uncertainty and a willingness to question in the forefront of his teaching. . . . while Carter empathized with the students' struggle to write he understood that his job was to teach them to do it. He didn't put them down for not enjoying writing or writing well, but he also did not let them off the hook. He had to help them appreciate the power and fulfillment of writing and he had to preserve each student's sense of self. (p. 118)

Continuing to Learn

Continuing to learn is something we all can do. This Teacher Note attempts only to introduce you to some authors and resources who can contribute to that learning. Many of the resources cited here include rich examples from classrooms that can evoke productive interaction when read and discussed with peers. You may have opportunities to take advantage of courses, seminars, or study groups, such as the one that Lawrence and Tatum (1997) describe, or to self-organize peer discussions of articles in the field.

Teachers can also pose their own questions and study their own classrooms. Writing brief case studies in which you raise your own questions about these issues in your teaching and then sharing your writing can be a rich source of learning. You might start by reading what other teachers have written about their own practice as they reflect on their teaching of diverse students. For example, in *What's Happening in Math Class?* (Schifter, 1996), Alissa Sheinbach writes about three students who are struggling in mathematics (vol. 1, pp. 115–129), Allen Gagnon writes about his Spanish-speaking students (vol. 1, pp. 129–136), and Nora Toney recounts her own experiences with racism as a student (when she was bused into a largely white school) and later as a teacher herself (vol. 2, pp. 26–36). After describing some successful experiences in mathematics she had as an adult that contrasted with her experience in the "low group" as a student, Toney concludes by identifying factors that have been important to her own learning:

> I have discovered the ingredients necessary for me to learn and achieve success: high teacher expectation, fairness, inclusiveness, engaging contextual material, constant monitoring and feedback, discussions/debates, and reflective writing. Generally speaking, I need numerous opportunities to connect my thinking and ideas to new concepts and ideas. These factors facilitated my *learning* of mathematics, so now I am trying to incorporate these same factors into *teaching* mathematics. (p. 36)

References and Additional Readings

Ball, D. (1997). What do students know? Facing challenges of distance, context, and desire in trying to hear children. In T. Biddle, T. Good, & I. Goodson (Eds.), *International handbook on teachers and teaching* (pp. 769–817). Dordrecht, Netherlands: Kluwer Press.

Ballenger, C. (1999). *Teaching other people's children: Literacy and learning in a bilingual classroom.* New York: Teachers College Press.

Cochran-Smith, M. (1995a). Uncertain allies: Understanding the boundaries of race and teaching. *Harvard Educational Review, 63,* 541–570.

Cochran-Smith, M. (1995b). Color blindness and basket making are not the answers: Confronting the dilemmas of race, culture, and language diversity in teacher education. *American Educational Research Journal, 32,* 493–522.

Duckworth, E. (1996). *"The having of wonderful ideas" and other essays on teaching and learning.* New York: Teachers College Press.

Entwistle, D., and Alexander, K. (1989). Early schooling as a "critical period" phenomenon. In K. Namboodiri & R. Corwin (Eds.), *Research in Sociology of Education and Socialization,* Volume 8, (pp. 27–55) Greenwich, CT: Jai Press.

Heath, S. B. (1983). *Ways with words: Language, life, and work in communities and classrooms.* New York: Cambridge University Press.

Hiebert, J., Carpenter, T. P., Fennema, E., Fuson, K. C., Wearne, D., Murray, H., et al. (1997). *Making sense: Teaching and learning mathematics with understanding.* Portsmouth, NH: Heinemann.

Hudicourt-Barnes, J. (2003). The use of argumentation in Haitian Creole science classrooms. *Harvard Educational Review, 73*(1), 73–93.

King, J. (1991). Dysconscious racism: Ideology, identity, and the miseducation of teachers. *The Journal of Negro Education, 60,* 133–146.

Ladson-Billings, G. (1994). *The dreamkeepers: Successful teaching for African American students.* San Francisco: Jossey-Bass.

Ladson-Billings, G. (1995). Toward a theory of culturally relevant pedagogy. *American Educational Research Journal, 32,* 465–491.

Ladson-Billings, G. (2002). I ain't writin' nuttin': Permission to fail and demands to succeed in urban classrooms. In L. Delpit & J. K. Dowdy (Eds.), *The skin that we speak: Thoughts on language and culture in the classroom* (pp. 107–120). New York: The New Press.

Lawrence, S. M., & Tatum, B. D. (1997). White educators as allies: Moving from awareness to action. In M. Fine, L. Weis, L. C. Powell, & L. M. Wong (Eds.), *Off white: Readings on race, power, and society* (pp. 333–342). New York: Routledge.

Lewis, A. (2003). *Race in the schoolyard: Negotiating the color line in classrooms and communities.* New Brunswick, New Jersey and London: Rutgers University Press.

Moschkovich, J. (1999). Supporting the participation of English language learners in mathematical discussions. *For the Learning of Mathematics, 19*(1), 11–19.

National Council of Teachers of Mathematics. (2000). *Principles and standards for school mathematics.* Reston, VA: Author.

Obidah, J., & Teel, K. M. (1996). The impact of race on cultural differences on the teacher/student relationship: A collaborative classroom study by an African American and Caucasian teacher research team. *Kansas Association for Supervision and Curriculum Development Record, 14,* 70–86.

Obidah, J., & Teel, K. M. (2001). *Because of the kids.* New York: Teachers College Press.

Paley, V. G. (1989). *White teacher.* Cambridge, MA: Harvard University Press.

Schifter, D. (1996). *What's happening in math class? Vol. 1: Envisioning new practices through teacher narratives ; Vol. 2: Reconstructing professional identities.* New York: Teachers College Press.

Titles of Grade 5 Teacher Notes by Unit

PART 7

Working with the Range of Learners

Preview

All teachers are faced with the challenge of meeting the needs of a range of learners in their classrooms. The range of learners can include students who struggle in certain areas of mathematics, those who excel in math, students who are English Language Learners, and students who have particular learning needs.

This section contains a series of case studies written by fifth-grade teachers from urban, suburban, and rural schools, telling how they implemented the *Investigations* program in their classrooms. The students in these classrooms vary on many dimensions, including gender, language, culture and ethnicity, and special needs. They present a range of strengths and needs in their prior experience with mathematics and their confidence in the classroom.

Through their writing, these teachers bring us into their classrooms and invite us to participate in how they think about supporting their range of learners. As they captured moments in time in their classrooms, the teachers did not intend to provide exemplary actions to be emulated or a how-to manual of what to do for particular students or with particular activities. Rather, they offer the kind of thinking teachers do as a matter of course in their teaching. Through the hundreds of interactions they have with their students each day, teachers try to understand what those students bring to their learning and how to support them in moving further. In these case studies, they share some of that thinking.

We collected these cases together in this book, rather than including them with the curriculum units, because they are not designed to illustrate "how to do" a particular activity. Rather, as a group, they provide examples and questions to inspire your own questioning and reflection. You may want to use this set of cases on your own or discuss them with a group of colleagues.

Keep in mind that each case provides only a glimpse into a teacher's classroom. Just as you would not expect anyone to understand the complexity of the issues you face in your own classroom from such a brief glimpse, the cases cannot provide all the background information you might need to understand a particular teacher's decision with a particular student on a particular day. But you do not need to know more detail to use these cases for your own professional development. Use them as starting points when considering similar issues that you face with your students. The questions at the end of each case provide a starting point for discussion. If you discuss these cases with colleagues in a cross-grade group, you will have even more examples to consider by combining the sets of cases from two or more grades.

The classroom cases are grouped into three themes, focusing on some of the most important issues teachers face as they work to meet the needs of their students. In the first section, "Setting Up the Mathematical Community," teachers write about how they create a supportive and productive learning environment in their classrooms. In the second section, "Accommodations for Learning," teachers focus on specific modifications they make to meet the needs of some of their learners. Because these teachers chose to write about particular students in their classrooms, the cases do not cover all the kinds of needs and accommodations you might encounter. However, even though the specific students discussed may differ from students in your own classroom, these teachers consistently found that accommodations they had made for one student often spilled over to benefit other students with related needs. In the last section, "Language and Representation," teachers share how they help students use representations and develop language to investigate and express mathematical ideas.

There is, of course, much overlap. Some cases illustrate ideas that could fall into more than one of these sections. You will find ideas from one section cropping up in the cases in other sections. For example, when teachers develop accommodations for learning, they are often using mathematical representations or helping students connect their language to the mathematical ideas.

Note: Pseudonyms have been used for all student and teacher names.

Summary of Cases

Setting Up the Mathematical Community

First Steps in Creating the Mathematics Community

Suzanne Wilcox shares how she begins the process of creating a classroom community.

The Deer in the Headlights

The students in Gretchen Hopkins' math class have an opportunity to express the fears and anxieties they have about math.

"We Didn't Do Math Like This in My Old School." Integrating a New Student

Marion Perkins shares how she helped a new student, coming from a traditional math program, transition into the mathematics community in her classroom.

Student Grouping That Enhances Learning

Kellie Sullivan shares the purposeful way she groups her students for a Math Workshop.

Accommodations for Learning

Helping All Students Learn Multiplication Combinations

Suzanne Wilcox describes how she helps students who still have not learned the basic multiplication combinations learn them in the context of making sense of multiplication.

The Case of Katie: Building Similar Polygons— Wow! It's So Big!

Maria Martinez-Roberts plans activities to help Katie access the mathematics in the *Measuring Polygons* unit and shares how Katie's work contributes to the class.

Language and Representation

The Case of Dontrell: Developing Literacy Skills Through Mathematics

Maria Martinez-Roberts shares how a nonreader's interest and strength in mathematics contributes to the development of his literacy skills.

What's the "Difference"?

Gretchen Hopkins shares how she helps an English Language Learner understand the mathematical meaning for the word *difference*.

Representing and Reasoning About Change

Maria Martinez-Roberts helps students build on their prior knowledge to develop language and representations for their work with patterns and functions.

Setting Up the Mathematical Community

First Steps in Creating the Mathematics Community

At the beginning of the school year, teachers begin creating a classroom environment that is inclusive of all participants and that allows all students to share ideas and listen to and learn from each other. An important component of this work is to provide meaningful contexts that encourage students, including those who do not feel confident in their math abilities or who opt to stay on the periphery, to share their thinking and build on each other's ideas. In this case, fifth-grade teacher Suzanne Wilcox shares the approach she uses on the first days of school to begin creating an inclusive mathematics community.

The first day of each new school year offers unique opportunities to bring together a new group of learners and establish a community in which each person can learn with and from others. As I greet my class in September, I always think about this and keep in mind my own goals as the students and I collectively establish this new learning community.

I know an opportunity to set the stage for this community will present itself early in the school year, but I never know exactly how or when. This year it happened within the first hour of the first school day! My 20 new students were organizing their desks and storing their books and supplies when I pointed out to them that they each had two big textbooks. In my effort to motivate them to take care of the books, I asked, "How much do you think each one costs? What is your estimate of their value?" Shaun was anxious to respond.

I know Shaun only through his older brother, who was a student in one of my previous classes. I am aware that Shaun has multiple learning challenges, a complicated educational plan, and a reputation for "acting up" in class and on the playground. I knew that I wanted Shaun to have a significant role as a learner early on in the class, so I immediately asked him to respond.

"Twenty bucks," he said. I responded by saying, "I think you're right, Shaun. These books are probably worth between 20 and 35 dollars." A little lesson was forming in my mind, and it was very connected to the creation of the learning community that I was hoping for. "So, if each of these books is worth about 20 dollars, how much do you think all of them are worth for all 20 students in our class?"

Several students responded. Molly, a student entirely new to me, at first gave the answer $40. I wrote the following equations on the board to help Molly.

$$2 \times 2 = 4$$
$$20 \times 2 =$$
$$20 \times 20 =$$

When Molly looked at the equations, she realized the answer to 20×20 is 400, not 40. I wrote on the board:

$$\$20 \times 20 \text{ books} = \$400$$

"Shaun said he thought each book was worth 20 dollars. Then Molly said there were 20 books at 20 dollars each, and we got $400. Are we done? Are these books worth 400 dollars?" Another student, Carl, raised his hand and suggested, "It's 800 dollars. I just doubled it. We have 2 books each, so the total is doubled."

I turned to the board and paused, asking, "So how could I record your thinking mathematically, Carl? Is that adding or multiplying or what, that doubling you did?"

"Multiplying," answered Carl. "It's like 400 times 2." I added that number sentence to the board and also used Carl's idea to add to the first equation:

$$\$400 \times 2 = \$800$$
$$\$20 \times 20 \text{ books} \times 2 \text{ books each} = \$800$$

I invited the class to think along with Carl and me, "So now we've got $20 \times 20 \times 2$, the way Molly started, and Carl's method of multiplying 400 by 2. Do these work?"

The discussion continued in this way, with the students building on each other's ideas. Many of the students seemed to become more and more intrigued as the discussion evolved. I decided to follow up on this interest by asking them to do some writing.

"I'd like you to turn to your notebooks and record what we have been thinking about here. Please write today's date and the heading, Textbooks, and write a few sentences about what we figured out about the value of our textbooks. You can record these number sentences and tell what Shaun told us, what Molly figured out, and how Carl thought about doubling." I added, "One of the things we are going to be doing this year is thinking about math ideas all together as a group and then also for ourselves. I think this conversation has been really interesting, so I'm going to write it down in my notebook as well."

I pulled my own notebook out, sat down beside a student and recorded the thinking illustrated by the equations on the board. As I looked around this new class, writing down their ideas, I was satisfied that we had at least begun to create the learning community that I envision.

Mrs. Wilcox actively looks for ways to engage her students in meaningful discussions around mathematics. One way she does this is to bring up questions that are about the class so that there is common ground. She involves not only the students already excited about math but also the students who are quieter and those who may not have the same level of confidence and competence as others. By recording students' ideas publicly and letting students know that she is keeping track of their thinking, she communicates to them that she values and attends to their ideas. In this way, Mrs. Wilcox begins the process of building a strong mathematical community.

Questions for Discussion

1. What mathematical behaviors, which are helpful in building a mathematics community, was Mrs. Wilcox modeling and supporting during this discussion?

2. Think about the ways in which you can involve a range of students in activities and problems that are meaningful to them. How can you take advantage of opportunities that arise early in the year that will help build a supportive math community in your classroom?

The Deer in the Headlights

In this case, Gretchen Hopkins gives her fifth-grade students an opportunity to express the fears and anxieties they have about math and to talk together about the kind of support and help they need.

At the beginning of every school year, I notice several students who have a "deer in the headlights" expression when I ask them for an answer to a problem. Even when I rephrase the question and break it down into simpler steps, these students remain frozen. I have found that many of these students are female. Some are English Language Learners who are new to having all their instruction in English. I have also found that sometimes they are new to the *Investigations* materials and may not have developed number sense or a repertoire of strategies to solve problems.

It takes patience, encouragement, and the building of small successes to break through this barrier of math fear. I have to remember to check in with these students frequently at the beginning of each new math unit. I have found that it helps to talk directly about this freezing-up problem and to try to figure out ways to work through it. I gathered a group of my students and asked them what it feels like when this happens to them. There was a torrent of responses.

Tabatha: I'm embarrassed.

Marisol: I sweat on my forehead! Sometimes I get mixed up with all the math words.

Dorothy: When I'm churning, it feels like I don't have any ears, and I'm locked in my own head.

Tabatha: Yeah, I don't feel like I'm in fifth grade. It's like I'm little again!

Teacher: You mean all those ideas are going through your head in math class?

Bethany: If math feels hard to me now, then I start thinking to myself, "Gosh, if it's this bad now, what will happen to me next year?

Teacher: So you're worrying about your whole future when this happens?

Noelle: Yes! I get hot and really embarrassed. I try to pay attention. I hear, but I don't get it, and it doesn't stick in my head. It's even scarier when other students are all raising their hands.

Teacher: So, I hear you saying that sometimes you feel embarrassed, or mixed up by all the words, or worried about next year. Or you think that the other kids know more than you. What helps? What can I do to get you back on track?

Kathy: I like it when you say, after the main lesson, "If anyone would like to work with me to be sure you're on the right track, then meet me at the back table."

Tabatha: Yeah, going into a separate group is helpful if you don't understand.

Teacher: You don't feel embarrassed by that?

Kathy: No, because other kids are there, too.

Teacher: Well, if that's okay for you, then why don't you just raise your hand and ask for help?

Bethany: You don't really know if you are the only one who doesn't get it, especially at the beginning of the year.

Teacher: What else can I do to help out? What do you think you can do to help yourselves?

Noelle: Sometimes you tell us that we should look in our *Student Math Handbook* to see examples of what other kids do. I forget about that sometimes.

Marisol: Me, too. But sometimes it helps me remember words that are hard.

Teacher: Okay, now that you're explaining about what works this year, what can you do for yourself next year when you are in sixth grade?

Noelle: Try to raise my hand.

Kathy: Talk to the teacher as early as you can so it doesn't build into a huge problem.

Dorothy: Try not to be scared. Everyone has problems of one sort or another. Get help early and don't give up.

Many students experience fears and anxiety about math. In this case, Mrs. Hopkins allows her students to talk about their fears. In doing so she learns more about her students' insecurities, what she is already doing that is working for them, and how she can encourage them to take more responsibility. The learners in her classroom realize they are not alone as they strive to understand and feel comfortable about math.

Questions for Discussion

1. What ways could Mrs. Hopkins build on this discussion to help students take more responsibility for their own learning? Are there additional supports that she might put in place for her students based on what she heard in this discussion?

2. How do your students express their fears and anxiety about math? What strategies do you use to encourage them to discuss these feelings and to help them develop self-confidence?

"We Didn't Do Math Like This in My Old School." Integrating a New Student

Being the new student in a classroom is never easy. This transition becomes even more challenging when it occurs in the middle of the school year and when the curriculum in the new school differs from what the student is accustomed to. In this case, Marion Perkins shares how she helped such a student transition into her classroom community.

Classroom communities change constantly as new students enter the classroom at varying points throughout the year. It can be challenging for teachers to help new students transition into the mathematical community during the year. This can be particularly challenging when the new student has a more traditional background in mathematics instruction.

Damien entered my class in the middle of the year. At first, he appeared to slip in without a problem. An avid football player, he made friends the first day on the playground. He appeared comfortable in class, smiling often and raising his hand to volunteer ideas.

Math class, however, created issues for Damien. After a week or so he often commented, "We didn't do math like this in my old school." He was confused by the alternate strategies students were sharing for adding numbers. For example, one day we were solving the problem $3,487 + 5,018$ when one student shared:

I added the 3,000 and 5,000 to get 8,000. Then I added the 400 to get 8,400. Next I added $87 + 10$ to get 8,497. Then I added 3 from the 8 to get 8,500 and then the 5 that was left to get an answer of 8,505.

I could see Damien's eyes glaze over as he listened to this strategy. Although he clearly thought of himself as a good student, his number sense was extremely weak, and he had no idea how to add even relatively small numbers in his head. For instance, one day I asked him, "How much would $85 + 20$ be?" and he couldn't figure it out without writing it down. I could tell that his self-confidence was waning as he became increasingly aware that what we were doing was very different from what he was accustomed to and that he didn't

have the prerequisite skills and number sense to do well. Compounding the problem was the fact that he missed about 10 days of school for a family vacation at a crucial point in our fraction study. I again heard him sigh and remark, "We never did any of this at my old school."

Although my students were helpful and encouraging, and we kept trying to include Damien in our math discussions, I wondered if it would ever happen. Damien was becoming quieter, more hesitant, and less willing to share ideas.

One day shortly after Damien returned from his vacation, several students were playing a game called *Fraction Track,* a game in which they move counters along number lines, marked in thirds, fourths, fifths, tenths, and so on. Using knowledge gained from playing that game, the students began to add and subtract fractions. Damien had missed a lot and was very confused, so I worked with him one on one to teach him the game and evaluate his thinking. I asked him, "What parts do you get, and what parts are still confusing about this game?"

"I don't get the fraction where the top is bigger," he answered, adding his regular refrain, "We never did anything like that in my old school."

"Let's play together and see what we can figure out," I suggested. We played for about 15 minutes, and I observed his quick and solid mathematical thinking. I could sense him building understanding as he played. At one point he had to play $\frac{7}{4}$. By this time he had become more comfortable working with improper fractions. He played $\frac{3}{4}$ on the fourths track and needed to use the rest up on another track. I wrote:

$$\frac{7}{4} - \frac{3}{4} =$$

"So you played the $\frac{3}{4}$," I said, "How much do you still have to play?"

Damien looked up completely baffled, and said, "I don't know."

"What are you thinking about?" I asked.

"I don't know which numbers to subtract," he answered. "We never did this at my old school."

"Well, let's think," I said. "You have $\frac{7}{4}$ and you used $\frac{3}{4}$." How many fourths would still be left to use?"

With that little clue, Damien kept going and figured it out. I realized, however, that he was still operating on a model of math class in which you must be taught every procedure before you can do anything. The idea that you can figure things out for yourself in math was still brand new to him.

Damien's progress from this point was uneven, but it was progress. A few days later his eyes sparkled as he raised his hand and searched for the words, slowly but confidently, to restate a classmate's conjecture about adding fractions with the same denominators. "I think the same as Matt," he said. "If the, uh, bottom number, the, uh, denominators are the same, you can just add the top numbers, the numerators, and get the answer." Significantly, Matt was one of his football buddies.

A week or so later Damien perked up when I announced one day that we would be adding decimals.

"You look happy," I remarked.

"Yes." He answered, with a smile, "we did do this at my old school. I know how to add decimals."

This time when we shared strategies, Damien eagerly raised his hand. "Adding decimals is easy," he said. "You just line up the numbers top to bottom. You line up the decimal points and add like usual. I learned this before."

"That's interesting." I said. "So you learned that you can just line up the decimal points and add and it will work?"

Damien's response was telling about his previous math education. "I don't know," he answered. 'That's just what you do. That's what I learned." Although I took some time later to work with Damien to try to help him understand why his method worked, he didn't seem interested. I wondered if he even cared to understand why, and I felt bad for him that his moment of confidence had not played out the way he might have wished.

However, several days later, Damien showed his emerging place in our mathematics community when several students were working on a decimal-division chart in which they found the decimal equivalents for each fraction ($\frac{1}{5}, \frac{2}{5}, \frac{3}{5}, \frac{4}{5}$, etc.) and looked for patterns. On that same day Damien had received our classroom award for "Making a Smooooooth Transition into His New School." When I was giving Damien his award, I had reminded the class of how easily he had fit into our class and the games at recess. I mentioned his friendliness and his positive attitude that made other kids want to be with him. He beamed at this recognition.

The students worked hard and with good concentration on their charts, first filling in the decimals they knew like 0.5 for $\frac{1}{2}$ and 0.75 for $\frac{3}{4}$. For ones they didn't know, they used calculators, recorded them, and looked for patterns. As the work progressed, I noticed Damien interacting eagerly with Kaitlin, a new group mate who likes math a lot and is especially friendly like he is. They were sharing ideas about patterns and clearly making some wonderful discoveries together. They were not getting distracted from the task, as Damien sometimes did when he did not understand what we were doing. Instead they were eagerly proceeding down a long chart, filling in numbers and discussing patterns they found.

When recess time arrived, most of the students had not finished the chart. I told them they could continue to work during silent reading after recess, if they chose to, in preparation for our discussion the next day. After recess, Kaitlin and Damien were once again huddled together over their papers, discussing patterns in hushed tones while other students were reading around them. I realized that Damien was finally feeling like a member of this community.

I am relieved and intrigued by Damien's progress as he becomes absorbed into the mathematics community of our classroom. Although I am not sure what helped him make the transition, I do believe that, if we are patient, the community can draw students in.

Ms. Perkins was determined to make Damien feel part of the mathematics community. When she spent individual time with him, he felt comfortable acknowledging that he had been taught math differently. This gave them a starting point, and she was able to probe his thinking, while acknowledging his numerous strengths in the classroom. His ease with social relationships allowed him to form productive partnerships with other students. The combination of teacher and peer support helped Damien become a part of the mathematical community.

Questions for Discussion

1. What specific support from Ms. Perkins and the students appeared to help Damien integrate into the math community?

2. How have you helped students who have come from traditional math programs to learn and participate in your math class?

Student Grouping That Enhances Learning

Student grouping for mathematics instruction is an area that has received widespread attention in recent years. Some educators believe that homogeneous (ability) grouping is a way to ensure that students obtain specific experiences and skills needed to move their thinking forward. Others feel that heterogeneous grouping offers students a chance to share their thinking across ability levels and therefore leads to increased understanding of concepts and topics for all students. In either case, educators must consider the intersection of mathematical content, student ability, and experiences when grouping students for mathematics instruction. They need to think about student grouping flexibly according to the demands of the task.

Kellie Sullivan describes her thinking about student grouping for a Math Workshop on multiplication. She bases her decisions on her students' unique mathematical and social contributions, personality, and disposition.

As I considered my students and thought about where they were in developing strategies for multiplication, I decided to partner them deliberately and have the partners remain together for the entire Math Workshop. Although I sometimes hear teachers talk about this sort of partnering as a form of ability grouping, I was thinking more of partnerships that would stimulate thinking and forward movement for each and every student. I thought about where students' thinking was at the moment, what sort of nudge I felt they needed to move forward, and which classmates might provide that opportunity.

As I introduced the activities to my students, I was quite explicit about the reasons for the partners. I said:

This Math Workshop will last several days, and I have chosen a partner for you who I think will help you learn in a certain way. Your partner may be someone who is thinking in the same way you are, so you can solve the problems together and help each other. Or your partner may be someone who thinks a bit differently and can show you a new and interesting way to solve the problems. Either way, your partner will help you learn.

For example, one of the partnerships that I formed was between Dan and Kalina, partly because they get along well together. While Kalina can be challenging for others to work with, her math skills are strong, and she is confident with multiplication cluster problems and thinking her way through them. Dan, on the other hand, often gets stuck and doesn't know how to start. He has the social skills to deal with Kalina's prickly personality, and she has the clarity of thinking to help Dan move forward mathematically.

I partnered Lesa and Nathan because Lesa was quite articulate and confident about strategies she had developed while working with our remedial math teacher, Ms. Richmond. Nathan needed to become more flexible in his strategies and more articulate about them. They were working on similar strategies, but I felt Lesa might help Nathan develop more flexibility, while she would benefit from the need to explain to him. Because they both liked to write, I expected they would enjoy developing their written explanations together. In addition, Lesa is able to stay on task during open-ended activities, and Nathan needs support to stay focused.

Chase and Jillian, both strong math thinkers, were partners. Chase has a difficult time explaining his thinking clearly and completely, while Jillian is comfortable sticking with writing her explanations until they are complete. I thought she would be challenged trying to understand his thinking, while he might progress in being able to explain his thinking.

Jamal and Tarana are two strong students whom I paired together. Both of them use the standard algorithm. Although they are usually successful in solving problems and both insisted they "like this way the best," I was convinced they were capable of thinking much more deeply and flexibly. I was concerned that they were not flexible in approaching problems and that they did not always look at the problem as a whole before trying to solve it. I also knew they could deepen their understanding of multiplication by trying some other methods. As I handed out their folders, I specifically addressed this issue privately with them:

I'm having you be partners because I want you to work together to figure out other good ways to solve these problems. I know you can both do them that way, but sometimes there are other efficient ways to solve this kind of problem. I want you to find them.

Interestingly, they both grinned and looked as if they meant to rise to the challenge.

Matt and Spencer both often have unconventional but mathematically sound ways to solve problems. They also both tend to make careless errors and arrive at incorrect answers. As they began to work, I addressed this issue with them:

I have put you together because you are both really good math thinkers, but you often get the wrong answer. I want you to check each other carefully. Make sure you understand each other's methods, and that you have the correct answer at the end.

As I watched all of the partners set to work, I was pleased with the energy and cooperation that was evident in the room. Each partnership had complementary skills that were helping them stay focused, get into the problems, and move along. Each evening I collected the folders and went through them, noting work completed and, especially, strategies used. Each new day, I gave specific instructions about my expectations to each set of partners. I made up a set of challenge problems for some groups of students whom I felt needed to extend their thinking.

However, I began to worry a bit about a couple of students, including Dan. Dan's written work did not indicate that he was able to solve the cluster problems independently, and I wondered if his partnership was really helping him as I had hoped. Dan had completed very little work, and, at one point, I observed his partner, Kalina, standing by Dan's desk and coaching him about what to write on his paper. This, combined with the fact that he did not include a written explanation with any of his work, made me wonder if he had just copied the answers from Kalina. The next day, I decided to regroup a few partners so I could work individually with Dan and some other students. As we sat at the back table, I was relieved to discover that Dan understood more than his written work indicated. He was solving the problem 6 × 50. When I asked him, "Can you tell me how you got these answers?" he easily responded with mathematically accurate and sensible explanations. I then said, "Write that down just the way you said it." Dan wrote:

I knew 3 × 50 = 150. Six is the doble [double] of 3, so I doubled the 150 to get 300.

As I reviewed the work of the remaining partners, I saw the growth I had been hoping for.

- Chase, with Jillian's support, had been able to write explanations for all of his problems, which he had been unable to do before.

- Lesa and Nathan, too, had finished all the pages and had time to play a game. Their work was complete, organized, and accurate.

- I smiled to note that Spencer and Matt had completed a good deal of work and, although I had asked them to correct a few things, for the most part their answers were clear and accurate.

- Although Tarana had been absent for part of the Math Workshop, she and Jamal had completed a good deal of work. Jamal, when given the chance to substitute challenge problems for the required work, moved ahead a good deal. He worked with sustained interest on the problems I had made up for him, figuring each one out before checking it with great pleasure on the calculator. He was demonstrating the flexibility that I had hoped he would develop in his strategies, even with very difficult problems.

As I thought back about the Math Workshop we had finished, I realized my own thinking about the purpose of the activities had evolved as well. I used to think Math Workshop was for practicing skills and strategies. This time, however, I had specifically identified places where each student needed to grow. I had chosen partners based on my assessment of all students. I thought about students who would inspire other students in their mathematical development, and I told students what I expected of their partnerships. Given those expectations and my own clarity about mathematical growth instead of just rote practice, I believe that my students accomplished more during those three days than might have otherwise been the case.

Cooperative grouping in mathematics can be an important strategy for enhancing learning, but all too often cooperative groups are formed without careful attention to the ways in which students might support each other's mathematical thinking. Grouping is sometimes done strictly according to mathematical ability or to create a mix of students in terms of gender, race and ethnicity, and language preferences. Sometimes groups are self-chosen so that many students consistently work with the same individuals.

Ms. Sullivan illustrates a more complex way of thinking about student groupings that takes into consideration students' mathematical abilities, as well as their personalities and her own mathematical goals for each student. Ms. Sullivan makes her expectations clear for students, reviews the purpose of the partnerships, provides regular check-ins, and alters pairings when they appear not to meet her expectations. Her approach provides students with numerous opportunities to work in a variety of thoughtfully chosen groupings.

Questions for Discussion

1. **What factors about her students did Ms. Sullivan take into account as she planned how to group them?**

2. **Why do you think she chose to make her decisions explicit to her students? Do you agree with this decision?**

3. **In what ways do you use flexible grouping to meet the needs of the students in your classroom? What factors do you take into account as you plan your groups?**

Accommodations for Learning

Helping All Students Learn Multiplication Combinations

The students in Suzanne Wilcox's class have come to her with a range of previous math experiences. The year is just beginning, and although it is expected that her fifth-grade students should have mastered their multiplication combinations by now, she realizes that this is not the case for all of her students. She needs to work with her students to find out why some of them are having difficulty. During the first month of school, she plans to devote a portion of each math class to multiplication combinations. An important part of her plan is to talk with each student to better determine what type of learner he or she is and to check on student progress.

First Week of School

When I looked at the completed *Student Activity Book* page 9, *Multiplication Combinations 1,* from Unit 1, *Number Puzzles and Multiple Towers,* I noticed that many of my students had not yet mastered their multiplication combinations. Several of my students were new to *Investigations* this year, and I needed to have a better sense of what multiplication combinations students knew and which ones they still needed to learn.

On *Student Activity Book* page 10, *Multiplication Combinations,* for homework, students record the combinations they are still working on and clues to help them learn those combinations. This is exactly what my students needed to do. However, since more of them than I expected seem to need work with their multiplication combinations, I decided to take this a step further.

I asked a fourth-grade colleague for a copy of Resource Masters M35–M40, *Multiplication Cards,* from Unit 1 in Grade 4, *Factors, Multiples, and Arrays.* I made copies for the students and asked them to sort their cards into multiplication combinations they knew and which ones they need to learn. Following that, I had each student select five multiplication combinations to work on for the week. Since I want my students to not simply memorize the facts but also to use what they already know to figure out the combinations that are more difficult for them, we spent some time as a

class discussing the clues that students could write on these cards. We started by looking at the example on *Student Activity Book* page 10, for the combinations 7×9 and 9×7. I wanted to see if students could explain the relationship between that combination and the clue "$7 \times 10 = 70$, $70 - 7 = 63$" that was written on the student sheet.

One student explained:

Well, I think about 7×9 as a seven added nine times, but that one is hard for me to remember. Yet I know that ten 7s is 70, so I can do $7 \times 10 = 70$ and then just subtract one 7 to get my answer.

Another showed this relationship on an array.

If you look at the 7×10 array, you can see the extra column of 7 that you subtract from 70 to find the product of 7×9.

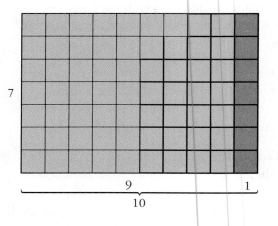

We discussed some other known combinations students might use to help them, before students moved on to writing clues for those combinations they still needed to learn. I also reminded students that they should refer to the Multiplication Combination pages in the *Student Math Handbook* for additional support. I observed the students as they worked and was pleased with what I saw. For example, one student, Samuel, was working on learning 9×8 and 8×9 and wrote the clue "$10 \times 8 = 80$, $80 - 8 = 72$" on the bottom of his card.

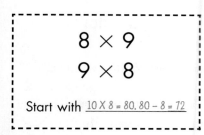

8×9

9×8

Start with $10 \times 8 = 80, 80 - 8 = 72$

Second Week of School

During the second week of school, I held short, individual conferences with my students. In my journal, I sorted the class into three groups.

1	**Students who know multiplication combinations well**	No need to conference with these students
2	**Students who know some combinations but have some left to learn**	Continue to meet and record their progress
3	**Students who are struggling with learning multiplication combinations**	Need to spend more time with these students to determine why they are having so much trouble and to think of ways I can help them

Third Week of School

I met with a few students whom I had identified as struggling to find out why learning their multiplication facts was such a challenge. Norm is such a student. I know he understands the concepts behind multiplication. He has had a lot of experience using arrays and is able to visualize a multiplication problem using this geometric model. Even though Norm is able to figure out the answer to multiplication problems by using arrays and skip counting, he does not have the fluency made possible by knowing the 1-digit multiplication combinations. I decided to work with him to develop fluency with multiplication facts by building on his knowledge of skip counting.

Another student, Allison, is new to the school. She has memorized many multiplication facts, but, as I worked with her individually, I found that Allison does not really understand how multiplication works or how to use the facts she knows to help her solve problems. I spent some time working with Allison to help her understand how arrays can be used to represent multiplication so that she can visualize what a multiplication situation looks like. I also had Allison make a skip counting book showing all the multiples of 2 through 10 on 100 charts. Allison uses both of these tools, arrays and skip counting charts, when working on multiplication problems so that she can develop a better visual and mental model of each problem. I want Allison to learn the rest of the multiplication facts within this more meaningful view of multiplication.

I continued to spend a portion of each math class working with all of the students on multiplication. I created a list on chart paper of the facts students learned during the previous week and their strategies for learning them and had the students pause to look at what they already have accomplished.

Fourth Week of School

By the fourth week of school, three fourths of the students knew all their multiplication facts. I continued to conference with those students who still had a few combinations left to master, making sure that they continued to use the multiplication cards with clues and that they were making steady progress. I know that a few students, like Norm and Allison, will need to keep working on their combinations, possibly for the rest of the year. However, I also know that understanding and modeling the operation of multiplication is central to their learning and should not be delayed by the need for continued work on combinations. Norm and Allison are developing good tools for solving multidigit multiplication problems, and, in this context, I will also continue to work with them on their multiplication combinations.

After recognizing that some of her students don't yet know all of the multiplication combinations, Mrs. Wilcox develops a plan that includes taking the time to become aware of their individual learning needs and styles. Students who may initially look the same—they have trouble solving multiplication problems or they do not know all their multiplication combinations—can have very different competencies and needs. Getting to know students as individual learners allows Mrs. Wilcox to determine how to best support each student in learning the combinations, while they continue, at the same time, to develop their understanding of multiplication.

Questions for Discussion

1. How does Mrs. Wilcox determine what each of her students needs to work on to best learn the multiplication combinations?

2. What are the strategies Mrs. Wilcox provides for students who are struggling to allow them to progress in both their knowledge of multiplication combinations and their understanding of the operation of multiplication?

3. Mrs. Wilcox states that working on the multiplication combinations should not be done in place of developing an understanding of multiplication and strategies for solving multiplication problems. It should be done in the context of this important work. Do you agree that these can happen simultaneously?

4. How have you balanced the need some students have to learn the basic combinations with their need to develop a deeper understanding of and increased efficiency with multiplication?

The Case of Katie: Building Similar Polygons—Wow! It's So Big!

As a teacher in a continuous learning model, Maria Martinez-Roberts "loops" with her students, teaching the same group for both fourth and fifth grades. In October of the fifth-grade year, her second year with this particular group of students, Ms. Martinez-Roberts finds herself thinking of how to meet the needs of her wide range of learners during the 2-D Geometry and Measurement unit, Measuring Polygons. *Her thoughts particularly focus on Katie, a student with a variety of sensory and learning challenges. She ponders how to balance the need to develop Katie's numerical skills and build on her visualization abilities while at the same time including her in the class work on geometry. From her work with the group in fourth grade, Ms. Martinez-Roberts is confident that her students have developed an appreciation of each other's ideas and the diverse strategies that develop from their collective thinking.*

Fifth-grade mathematical ideas are challenging for some of my learners to access. I have to think about ways to help them develop their mathematical ideas so they can engage and participate in whole-class activities and discussion, for which the majority of students have entry points. Katie is a student who had only learned how to distinguish letters from numbers in the fall of her fourth-grade year. How could I develop accommodations that would balance her present mathematical needs and the need to have her feel a part of our mathematical learning community?

Early in the fourth-grade year, I had noted that Katie had strong spatial visualization skills and that she often chose geometrically based tasks when she had a choice. I knew that these strengths could assist her in developing her numeric reasoning. Because Katie was not yet able to access most text independently (and could therefore not read directions on her own), it was also important that she develop a repertoire of games and tasks that provided her with opportunities to engage in number and shape work. To help Katie become more independent and to have a choice of valuable mathematical tasks, I spent a lot of time with her playing games from the lower grades of *Investigations,* such as *Capture Five, Compare Dots, Towers of Ten,* and *On and Off.* She kept a variety of these games in a basket near her desk. These games allowed her to continue to develop the number ideas she needed and also provided a basis for entering games that she might play with her peers, such as *Count and Compare with Arrays*.

During one particular Math Workshop, I was again reminded of the importance of the work we had done to establish a respect for all voices. The class had been analyzing the properties of polygons for several days. The students had constructed polygons with Power Polygons and on coordinate grids. The language of mathematics was important in this work as students developed working definitions for shapes and kept track of these on class charts. There was lots of discussion in the formation, application, and evaluation of these definitions. Katie would listen intently to these discussions as she worked on her own book of shapes and words. She had been able to use much of this vocabulary as she worked with a heterogeneous group on a sorting and classifying game that included a variety of triangles and quadrilaterals.

The class moved to investigating angle size and turns, but the number work became an obstacle for Katie. Anticipating that our next focus would be on constructing similar polygons, I prepared templates (outlines of polygons made up of Power Polygons) for Katie. She spent several days finding the smaller polygon shapes that would cover the shapes outlined on the templates and counting the number of smaller shapes she used each time. Some of her templates were of one Power Polygon and then similar polygons (see Figure 1) that she had to construct with a number of the original Power Polygon shape. Other templates were of one Power Polygon and then a similar figure (see Figure 2) constructed from a mix of Power Polygon shapes.

Figure 2

By the time the class completed the work with angles and turns, Katie had spent a lot of time exploring the collection of polygons and decomposing and recomposing shapes.

The class was now moving to an investigation of similar figures. The big idea I wanted students to encounter and make sense of was the proportional relationship between similar figures. Would they note how changing the length of the sides impacted the area? Students were working in groups to construct similar figures and using a table that kept track of the number of the original shape pieces it took to construct a new similar shape. There was a low buzz of voices and discussion about the number patterns that students noticed as they built each series of similar shapes. Suddenly, we heard Katie's voice boom out from under her desk. "Wow! Look how big it got!" As I walked over, I noticed that she had used one of the nonregular polygon templates I had created, a "house" composed of a square with a triangle on top, and had continued to add to it until there was a large area of the carpet covered by a similar figure! (See figure 3.)

Figure 1

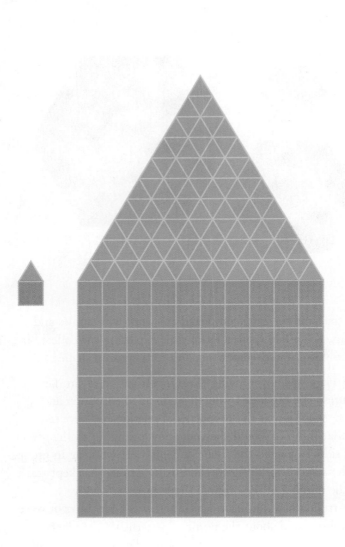

Figure 3

multiplicative nature of the area of the new figures would have been as rich without Katie's excitement and representation. What was the power of her representation? And how did it influence the work the rest of the class would engage in? And how did the reactions of her classmates to her work impact Katie's disposition toward mathematics and her willingness to engage with ideas that might be just beyond her reach?

This case is an example of how a range of learners can support each other's understandings regardless of the differences in initial levels of understanding. I am left wondering: What is the role of community and communication in the course of developing significant ideas? How do I continue to support the development of those ideas for the range of learners in my classroom?

In this case, Ms. Martinez-Roberts planned experiences for Katie to help her access the mathematical concepts in the Measuring Polygons *unit. By participating in these activities, Katie was able to develop her understanding of similar shapes and make sense of the mathematical language in the unit. In turn, the class was able to value and build on Katie's work.*

Questions for Discussion

1. **What were Ms. Martinez-Roberts's mathematical goals for the session, for both Katie and the whole class?**

2. **How did the experiences that Ms. Martinez-Roberts planned for Katie help her build mathematical understanding in both numerical relationships and geometric concepts?**

3. **Ms. Martinez-Roberts had worked to develop a community of learners who valued each other's thinking. What steps have you taken in your classroom to encourage students to support each other?**

My students gathered around Katie's work and were soon caught up in her excitement about the bigness of her representation. (One student commented that Katie's figure could be broken into a figure similar to the original square and another figure similar to the original triangle.) Needless to say, soon our classroom floor was literally covered with a collection of similar figures that were "wow, so big!" and students were investigating what was happening to the number patterns they had noticed earlier with the smaller similar figures. I wonder if the idea of similarity and the

Language and Representation

The Case of Dontrell: Developing Literacy Skills Through Mathematics

Working with students who have a variety of needs is always challenging and is compounded when one of those needs is limited reading ability. The shift in literacy instruction in the upper grades from "learning to read" to "reading to learn" necessitates that teachers help students with literacy problems to find entry points into all areas of the curriculum, including mathematics. In the following case, Maria Martinez-Roberts reflects on one of her students who begins the school year as a nonreader. She shares how his interest and strength in mathematics contributes to the development of his literacy skills and how the development of his literacy skills enables him to continue to grow mathematically.

Dontrell, a quiet, shy boy with a myriad of learning and emotional difficulties, joined our class community a few months into the school year. He was a nonreader, working at the preprimer level, and had language delays that made oral communication difficult and written communication even more so. Both physical and emotional factors affected Dontrell's ability to focus and make academic progress. While Dontrell was polite and tried to do his best, he often became frustrated and would retreat into an "I can't do this" stance.

Within a few days of his arrival, I noted that Dontrell looked forward to our mathematics time. He would lift his head off his desk and listen to the other students share their thinking. He would not make attempts to record any of his thinking with number or word representations, but he was beginning to "read" the work of his classmates. One day when I crouched near his desk and asked him what he thought about Lexi's strategy for solving 23 × 4, he stated,

I think she likes to use 20 first. But I would use 25 four times and then subtract two 4s.

As we moved to solving multiplication problems with larger numbers, Dontrell began raising his hand to share his thinking. I was amazed at his ability to hold all his steps in his head and articulate each step without writing anything down. He was showing evidence of strong numeric reasoning and was beginning to feel confident sharing his ideas.

On one particular day, I gave each group of students a transparency on which to represent their strategies for solving a multiplication problem. I asked each group to discuss their individual strategies, come to a group consensus on one strategy they wanted to share, and record that strategy in their individual journals before preparing their transparency. As I walked over to Dontrell's group, I noticed that he had not only recorded his team's strategy but had also drawn an array and written several sentences about his strategy. This was the first time that he had attempted to do any writing! Dontrell proudly shared his group's thinking at the overhead.

As the weeks passed, I began to use Dontrell's math ideas for his literacy work. One of his classmates or I would write his ideas in his journal and then he would practice reading "my words and my thinking." We made cards for words that he used often, such as "break apart," "took away," "friendly number," and "close to my number." Dontrell's fascination with numbers and his pride in his ability to solve problems gave him the confidence to attempt more reading and writing activities. He enjoyed writing stories that represented multiplication and division situations. He would sometimes read a short picture book and then rewrite the story as a math problem. Dontrell shared with me that he now thought math was fun because he liked how we "talked about math and did the math in lots of different ways."

As spring and the end-of-the-year state assessments approached, our class began discussing test-taking skills. Our mathematics end-of-grade test would consist entirely of word problems. Despite Dontrell's reading difficulties, he would not be allowed any testing modifications due to a variety of factors, including timing, the particularities of our state's special education laws, and the irony of his testing above his cognitive level. I knew that Dontrell was a strong mathematical thinker with flexible and efficient strategies for computing. His spatial visualization skills and oral geometric language were also at grade level benchmarks. However, despite the progress he had made in decoding words and comprehending text, I wondered how he would be able to sustain and interpret the mathematical ideas amidst all the reading he would have to do during the nearly $2\frac{1}{2}$-hour mathematics test. How would he navigate through words such as *approximately* and *estimate* and *perpendicular* and all the words that provided the context for the math problems he would have to solve?

I felt certain, based on my observations and his formative and summative assessments throughout the school year, that Dontrell would be able to be successful with the next grade's course of study in mathematics. When the end-of-grade testing results arrived, I was delighted to see that he had scored in the top scale in mathematics, with the sixth highest score in our class of 26 students! Clearly, his love of mathematics had provided the incentive he needed to tackle the difficult reading that the test included.

Dontrell had clearly come far since arriving in our classroom, but much work remained. Although he had done very well in the mathematics assessment, he had not passed the end-of-grade reading assessment. As I celebrated the progress that this fragile learner had made, I reflected on the role that his mathematical ability had on his cognitive, affective, and social development. I was left with questions about the work of building on his mathematical ability to develop his literacy skills, and how this work could continue. For example,

- How had his positive disposition, number fluency, and competence in mathematics affected his literacy fluency?

- What strategies does a fragile reader employ to make sense of the mathematical ideas embedded in the words that he or she cannot decode or comprehend?

- How does the processing of mathematical ideas support the semantic and syntactical processes needed to read and comprehend text?

- What more could I and Dontrell's future teachers do to take advantage of the opportunities for literacy development that his mathematical strengths provide?

It is critical to identify the strengths of students who have special needs in some areas. In this case, Ms. Martinez-Roberts recognized Dontrell's strengths in mathematical reasoning and built on these strengths to increase his understanding both in mathematics and in reading.

Questions for Discussion

1. How did Ms. Martinez-Roberts use Dontrell's number fluency and competence in mathematics to develop his literacy skills?

2. How did the development of these skills impact the growth of Dontrell's mathematical confidence and understanding?

3. What experiences have you had teaching mathematics to students with limited literacy skills? In what ways have you been able to connect mathematics and literacy while keeping the focus on making meaning for both?

What's the "Difference"?

Teachers must be aware of the various ways students may interpret ideas during mathematical discussions. The fact that some words have multiple meanings can be tricky for students, particularly so for English Language Learners. These multiple meanings exist within everyday English usage, but such meanings are even more difficult for students to learn when there are differences between how a word is used in the everyday vernacular and how that same word is used in a mathematical sense. For example, in everyday usage, the word similar *means "resembling, without being identical" as in "John and Jose have similar haircuts." In mathematics, on the other hand, the word* similar *is a geometric term that refers to shapes "having the same shape, with the same angles and proportions, though not necessarily of the same size."*

As students develop mathematical terminology, they continue to refine their understanding of the mathematical meaning of particular words. As they do so, teachers need to understand the multiple registers in which their students move to facilitate communication, understand their work, and more accurately assess their understanding of mathematical concepts.[1]

In the following case, fifth-grade teacher Gretchen Hopkins shares with us an English Language Learner's confusion around the word difference.

Carmelo is a quiet and shy fifth-grade student who has been in this school since kindergarten. He speaks Spanish at home. Many new things are happening for him this year: He no longer receives ELL services in school, and he is working with the *Investigations* curriculum for the first time.

I have noticed that when I try to engage Carmelo in mathematical discourse, he is not able to use much math terminology and usually ducks his head in embarrassment. When I do get him to explain his ideas, he mostly talks around the subject, and I end up guessing his meaning and trying to fit it into the discussion that is going on. When I ask Carmelo questions to confirm my understanding of what he means, he invariably nods in agreement. I'm getting the

sense more and more that he will agree with anything I say as long as he can then hop off the hot seat. Just like the teacher in Judit Moschkovich's article, I think that there is sometimes a discrepancy between what he is trying to articulate and what I am assuming he is referring to.

A clear example of that discrepancy occurred when Carmelo was working on a homework assignment involving the *Digits Game.* The students were given three different sets of digits; they selected numbers from each set to write a number as close as possible to 2,500. Carmelo was able to arrange the digits to make numbers that were reasonably close (though not necessarily the closest) to 2,500:

> He used 1, 2, 6, 1, and 3 to make 2,611.
>
> He used 2, 9, 0, 6, and 4 to make 2,604.
>
> He used 8, 9, 4, 3, and 3 to make 3,438.

However, when he was asked to determine the difference between his numbers and the target, 2,500, he wrote:

> 6, 11
>
> 6, 4
>
> 3, 4, 3, 8

I was confused by this response until I realized that Carmelo was not interpreting the word *difference* in the mathematical sense of subtraction but was thinking about it in terms of the common, everyday sense of "not alike." He wrote all of the digits that were different from, that is, "not like," the digits in 2,500.

Even after 5 years of English instruction in school, there are many discrepancies between what I think Carmelo understands and what he actually understands. Is he confused about the vocabulary, the concept, or both? In examining Carmelo's work through this new lens, I realize that I need to make accommodations to address the confusions that arise for him as he negotiates between the mathematical and everyday registers in Spanish and English and between the

---

[1] Moschkovich, Judit. 1999. Supporting the participation of English language learners in mathematical discussions. In *For the Learning of Mathematics,* vol. 19, no. 1, 11–19.

two languages. For example, in the activity described here, my plan is to do the following:

- See if Carmelo can solve these problems if I rephrase the questions to clarify the term *difference* and say, for example, "How much more is 2,604 than 2,500?"

- Explain to Carmelo how I intended to use the word *difference* in this context.

- Ask him to place the number he wrote and the target number of 2,500 on a number line and connect the two to give him an image of the difference between the two numbers.

I need to help Carmelo move to a clearer understanding of mathematical vocabulary as it relates to his understanding of math concepts. I am going to have to make a more concerted effort to put him at ease in our math discussions so he will take more risks in describing his ideas and in the process develop more fluency with math terminology.

As Mrs. Hopkins took the time to understand Carmelo's unexpected response to a homework activity, she realized that he didn't understand the intention of the question he was asked. This insight into Carmelo's mistake allowed Mrs. Hopkins to become more aware of the multiple ways students understand and use math terminology. While English speakers go through the process of negotiating between the everyday and mathematical registers, among English Language Learners the process is more complex. Not only do English Language Learners need to negotiate between these two registers in English; they also need to do so between the two registers in their first language and between their first language and English.

Questions for Discussion

1. **What next steps might Mrs. Hopkins put in place to help Carmelo more comfortably and confidently communicate his mathematical ideas? How can she help Carmelo develop an understanding of terms within a mathematical context?**

2. **In what ways do you build in opportunities to check for understanding for yourself and the students in your classroom? How are you able to distinguish between difficulties students have with the mathematics and difficulties they may have with the language of instruction?**

Representing and Reasoning About Change

Maria Martinez-Roberts teaches in an inclusion classroom. As a teacher in a continuous learning model, she "loops" with her students, teaching the same group of students for both fourth and fifth grades. In Grade 4, the students collected data and constructed graphs. Now in Grade 5, her students are beginning Unit 8, Growth Patterns. *Ms. Martinez-Roberts recognizes the importance of helping them connect to and build on their prior knowledge to meet the challenges the work of this unit presents to the range of learners in her classroom.*

Realizing that my students benefit from having access to a history of their thinking, it is our practice to keep charts of our conjectures, developing language and representations on an easel as we progress through a unit of study. I often see students flip through this collection of charts during Math Workshop or as they work on new problems. I hoped that these charts would prove to be a critical and vital part of the discussions that evolved as we progressed through our work with patterns, functions, and change.

Approximately one fourth of this class has language development challenges, making it even more important to provide a clear link between the informal language with which the students are familiar and the language of mathematics that will allow us to have meaningful discourse. My students need to use their informal or familiar language to express their ideas, and they need multiple opportunities to integrate that language with the formal language of mathematics.

To prepare for this unit of study, we created a chart of describing words for graphs. I posted a three-column chart with the following headings: "Describing Words We Know,"

"Representations," and "New Words We Can Use." Since the first Investigation begins with children's growth stories, I asked my students to recall how they had kept track of their own height in fourth grade and the graphs that they had made. Several students also mentioned the graphs we had created this year during our study of landforms and weather. Under "Describing Words We Know," my students contributed this list:

Describing Words We Know

Going up

Going down

Jagged

Mountains

Straight line

Close together

Far apart

Almost straight up

Almost straight down

Uneven

Even

No pattern

Changes a lot

Getting bigger

Getting smaller

Different students came up and drew a small representation next to each of the words. When we were done, we had established an anchor chart from which to begin some of our discussions. We then began constructing tables and graphs from the data of two imaginary children's growth patterns.

Later that day, when I revisited the chart, I noticed that most of these words seemed to be static words—words that described an overall result. I wanted to move my students to observing the dynamic part of the graphs. How did the graphs show change? How could we describe that change? As my students explored the situations involving functional relationships, they would be making quantitative observations, qualitative observations, and graphical observations. How would they develop their abilities to reason, represent, and communicate their observations? What would my role be in introducing new vocabulary? When and how would I introduce words such as *rate, slope, steep, steady, increase,* and *decrease*?

One answer to that question came during a discussion in which we were examining the growth of Tara and Nat, two children described in the unit. The students were observing the changes by looking at both the tables and the graphs. One student mentioned that the numbers showing Nat's height were changing quickly (+12, +13), and then slowly (+5, +5, +5). Another student came up and pointed to where those descriptions were evident in the graph. This was an opportunity to add two new words to our chart. As I flipped to the chart and began to add *slowly* and *quickly,* one of my students said, "Hey, that graph looks like the topography map we did for the sides of the mountain. It is really steep!"

This particular student was referring to mountain structures we had built from layers of foam. We had then transferred the concrete models to topography maps. I had not myself made the connection that the vocabulary we had used in that unit would be useful as we moved into examining functional relationships! We had kept one of the models on our science table, and one of my students rushed over to pick it up. We turned the model over until we could all see the side of the mountain that was very steep. I asked one of the students to use his fingers "to walk" up the side of the mountain. The class began to excitedly call out that he would have to walk almost straight up because he would have to take a big step up. We then looked at the other side of the mountain, which had a gentle slope. Another student came up and "walked" her fingers up the side of the mountain. She was able to take smaller steps as she walked up the layers. Although I knew that my students could sometimes be misled by interpreting a graph of change over time as showing the shape of some physical situation (e.g., misinterpreting a graph of the speed of a bicycle as showing the shape of the *course* of the bicycle), it seemed to me that in this case they used the physical model to ground their thinking about the meaning of steepness on a graph. By touching the sides of the mountain, they experienced directly how a steeper part of a graph involves a greater vertical change than a less steep part, relative to the same horizontal change—as some students expressed it, "the steeper it is, the farther apart are the numbers."

I called the students' attention back to the graphs and the tables we had been examining. I drew in steps to show how the line describing Nat's height was changing and asked the students to talk in their groups about how the steps in the graph related to climbing the mountain.

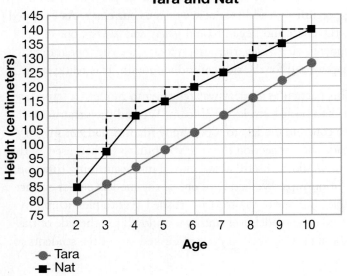

Tara and Nat

As the students' voices buzzed, I heard many new words used in their descriptions. They were also looking at our words chart, and several students were drawing representations of lines in their journals to help reinforce what they were describing orally to their teammates. When we came back together as a whole class, I asked the students what new words they wanted to add to the chart.

The following list was compiled and added to the "New Words We Can Use" column:

New Words We Can Use

Steep

Gentle

Curvy

Sloping

Changing slowly

Changing quickly

Same speed

The steeper it is, the farther apart are the numbers

The less steep it is, the closer are the numbers

Increase

Decrease

As I looked at the list, I noticed that these words were describing the changes they were noticing and also included two generalizations. It seemed that the three-dimensional model of the mountain and the action of walking had illuminated the actions that might not have been visible and thus not easily accessible to communicate in the two-dimensional graphical representations.

Our work then continued with investigations into the growth patterns of imaginary animals from the Planet Rhomaar that grew in predictable ways. As students began this work with linear functions, I was interested in how they would incorporate the new language into their discussions and writing.

As the work began, I noticed immediately how excited and engaged my students were. I was surprised and pleased at how much sharing and clarification of ideas was coming from some of my students who generally struggled with number work! The students in my classroom were integrating the common language we had developed into both their oral and written justifications and explanations. Words such as *pattern, steady, constant, predictable, expected,* and *persistent* were added to our chart. As students wrote about and represented their ideas, these ideas moved quickly throughout the room. Not only were students' written explanations full of the vocabulary we had constructed; they also included moves to symbolic expressions.

Dustin wrote:

The Krink was 1 cm at birth. He grows 5 cm a year. He grows at a steady rate. I know I can count on him growing the same every year. This is how I know: age # $\times$ 5 + 1 = height.

AJ wrote:

On my animal's second birthday, he was 90 cm. He grew very fast until he was 7; you can see it on the line. That is when he started to grow slower but still steady.

Emily wrote:

The Krink was 1 cm at birth. He grows at a steady pace. I can predict his height at any age: A $\times$ 5 + 1 = height.

Meg wrote:

The Krink will never catch up to Water Weasel because at age 10 the Water Weasel is already 65 cm, and the Krink is only 51 cm. They are both growing the same speed, steady at 5 cm but one started at 1 cm, that's the Krink, and the other started at 15 cm. So even though their graphs look the same steepness, the Water Weasel is always on top of the Krink. The Krink: A $\times$ 5 + 1; the Water Weasel: A $\times$ 5 + 15. A = age.

I continue to reflect on the factors that allow all my students an entry point into these algebraic ideas:

- The importance of having partner and small-group discussions so that many voices are engaged in the talking of mathematics

- The importance of immersing students in words that are familiar and that can be connected to their background knowledge

- The importance of assisting students in connecting words to experiences, actions, models, and representations

- The importance of establishing well-grounded and conceptual understandings before moving to symbolic representations

- The importance of trusting that the students' ideas can be the entry into developing the language of mathematics

Ms. Martinez-Roberts is aware of the diverse needs in her class. Before starting a new topic in mathematics, she considers what prior experiences students have had and finds out what language students know to describe relevant mathematical ideas. By listing her students' words and phrases, she both acknowledges their informal language and provides a structure for working on developing language that can describe these ideas more clearly and accurately.

Questions for Discussion

1. What prior knowledge did Ms. Martinez-Roberts hope her students would connect to and build on as they began their work with patterns and functions? What structures did she put in place to help her students make these connections?

2. How does Ms. Martinez-Roberts help them expand their language to the more clearly describe mathematical ideas? What opportunities does she provide her students to connect representations to the vocabulary they have generated? How do Ms. Martinez-Roberts's strategies provide a variety of entry points for the range of learners in her class?

3. What structures do you put in place in your classroom when moving to a new topic of study to help the range of learners in your classroom connect to and build on prior knowledge?

Scope and Sequence

The strands are divided into Math Emphases.

The Math Emphases may be covered in one or more units. The Math Emphases are further subdivided into Math Focus Points.

GRADE 5

Number and Operations

Each strand is labeled with a grade level.

The content is organized around five strands.

Whole Number Operations Reasoning about numbers and their factors

Unit 1 Math Focus Points

- Determining whether one number is a factor or multiple of another
- Identifying prime, square, even and odd numbers
- Using known multiplication combinations to find equivalent multiplication combinations (e.g., $18 = 3 \times 6 = 3 \times (2 \times 3)$)
- Using known multiplication combinations to find multiplication combinations for numbers related by place value (e.g., $3 \times 6 = 18$; $3 \times 6 \times 10 = 180$)
- Finding all the ways to multiply whole numbers for a given product
- Finding all the factors of a number
- Using properties (even, odd, prime, square) and relationships (factor, multiple) of numbers to solve problems
- Determining the prime factorization of a number

GRADE 4

Number and Operations

Whole Number Operations Understanding and working with an array model of multiplication

Unit 1 Math Focus Points

◆ Using arrays to model multiplication situations

◆ Breaking an array into parts to find the product represented by the array

◆ Using arrays to find factors of 2-digit numbers

◆ Identifying features of numbers, including prime, square, and composite numbers

Whole Number Operations Reasoning about numbers and their factors

Unit 1 Math Focus Points

◆ Finding the multiples of a number by skip counting

◆ Determining whether one number is a factor or multiple of another

◆ Identifying the factors of a given number

◆ Identifying all the factors of 100

◆ Using knowledge of the factors of 100 to find factors of multiples of 100

◆ Using known multiplication combinations to find related multiplication combinations for a given product (e.g., if $4 \times 50 = 200$, then $8 \times 25 = 200$)

◆ Using representations to show that a factor of a number is also a factor of its multiples (e.g., if 25 is a factor of 100, then 25 is also a factor of 300)

Unit 3 Math Focus Points

◆ Understanding the effect of multiplying by a multiple of 10 (e.g., describing the relationship between 3×4 and 3×40)

◆ Finding multiples of 2-digit numbers

◆ Describing a sequence of multiples in order to predict other multiples

◆ Determining the effect on the product when a factor is doubled or halved

Whole Number Operations Understanding and using the relationship between multiplication and division to solve division problems

Unit 3 Math Focus Points

◆ Solving division story problems

◆ Using and interpreting division notation

◆ Solving division problems by making groups of the divisor

◆ Using known multiplication combinations to solve division problems

Unit 8 Math Focus Points

◆ Representing a multiplication or division problem with pictures or diagrams, including arrays and pictures of groups

◆ Using a story problem represented by a multiplication expression to keep track of parts of the problems

Whole Number Operations Describing, analyzing, and comparing strategies for adding and subtracting whole numbers

Unit 5 Math Focus Points

◆ Representing addition and subtraction on a number line

◆ Identifying, describing, and comparing addition and subtraction strategies by focusing on how each strategy starts

◆ Developing arguments about why two addition expressions are equivalent (e.g., $597 + 375 = 600 + 372$)

◆ Using story contexts and representations to support explanations about equivalent addition expressions

◆ Understanding the meaning of the steps and notation of the U.S. algorithm for addition

◆ Developing arguments about how the differences represented by two subtraction expressions are related (e.g., 432 − 198 and 432 − 200)

◆ Using story contexts and representations to support explanations about related subtraction expressions

Whole Number Operations **Understanding different types of subtraction problems**

Unit 5 Math Focus Points
◆ Understanding the action of subtraction problems
◆ Representing subtraction situations

Whole Number Operations **Representing the meaning of multiplication and division**

Unit 3 Math Focus Points
◆ Representing a multiplication or division problem with pictures, diagrams, or models
◆ Using arrays to model multiplication
◆ Making sense of remainders in terms of the problem context
◆ Creating a story problem to represent a division expression
◆ Comparing visual representations of multiplication situations

Whole Number Operations **Understanding division as making groups of the divisor**

Unit 8 Math Focus Points
◆ Solving division problems by breaking the problem into parts
◆ Using multiples of 10 to solve division problems
◆ Using the relationship between multiplication and division to solve division problems

The Base-Ten Number System **Extending knowledge of the number system to 10,000**

Unit 5 Math Focus Points
◆ Reading, writing, and sequencing numbers to 1,000 and 10,000
◆ Understanding the structure of 10,000 and its equivalence to one thousand 10s, one hundred 100s, and ten 1,000s
◆ Recognizing the place value of digits in large numbers

Computational Fluency **Fluency with multiplication combinations to 12 × 12**

Unit 1 Math Focus Points
◆ Identifying and learning multiplication combinations not yet known fluently
◆ Using known multiplication combinations to determine the products of more difficult combinations

Computational Fluency **Solving multiplication problems with 2-digit numbers**

Unit 3 Math Focus Points
◆ Developing strategies for multiplying that involve breaking apart numbers
◆ Reviewing multiplication combinations to 12 × 12
◆ Multiplying multiples of 10

Unit 8 Math Focus Points
◆ Estimating solutions to 2-digit multiplication problems
◆ Multiplying multiples of 10
◆ Solving 2-digit multiplication problems by breaking a problem into smaller parts and combining the subproducts
◆ Solving 2-digit multiplication problems by changing one factor to create an easier problem

Computational Fluency **Adding and subtracting accurately and efficiently**

Unit 5 Math Focus Points

- Adding and subtracting multiples of 10, 100, and 1,000
- Using multiples of 10 and 100 to find the difference between any 3-digit number and 1,000
- Adding 3- and 4-digit numbers
- Using clear and concise notation for recording addition and subtraction strategies
- Finding combinations of 3-digit numbers that add to 1,000
- Solving subtraction problems by breaking numbers apart
- Solving multistep addition and subtraction problems
- Combining positive and negative numbers

Rational Numbers **Understanding the meaning of fractions and decimal fractions**

Unit 6 Math Focus Points

- Finding fractional parts of a rectangular area
- Finding fractional parts of a group (of objects, people, etc.)
- Interpreting the meaning of the numerator and the denominator of a fraction
- Writing, reading, and applying fraction notation
- Representing fractions greater than 1
- Identifying everyday uses of fractions and decimals
- Reading and writing tenths and hundredths
- Representing tenths and hundredths as parts of an area

Rational Numbers **Comparing the values of fractions and decimal fractions**

Unit 6 Math Focus Points

- Identifying relationships between unit fractions when one denominator is a multiple of the other (e.g., halves and fourths, thirds and sixths)
- Comparing the same fractional parts of different-sized wholes
- Identifying equivalent fractions
- Ordering fractions and justifying their order through reasoning about fraction equivalencies and relationships
- Representing fractions using a number line
- Comparing fractions to the landmarks $0, \frac{1}{2}, 1$, and 2
- Ordering decimals and justifying their order through reasoning about representations and meaning of the numbers
- Identifying decimal and fraction equivalents

Computation with Rational Numbers **Using representations to add rational numbers**

Unit 6 Math Focus Points

- Using representations to add fractions that sum to 1
- Estimating sums of fractions
- Adding fractions with the same and related denominators (e.g., halves, fourths, and eighths; thirds and sixths)
- Estimating sums of decimal numbers
- Adding decimal numbers that are multiples of 0.1 and 0.25 (e.g., $2.3 + 3.25$)
- Using representations to combine tenths and hundredths

GRADE 4

Patterns, Functions, and Change

Using Tables and Graphs Using graphs to represent change

Unit 9 Math Focus Points

- Interpreting the points and shape of a graph in terms of the situation the graph represents
- Finding the difference between two values on a line graph
- Discriminating between features of a graph that represent quantity and those that represent changes in quantity
- Plotting points on a coordinate grid to represent a situation in which one quantity is changing in relation to another
- Identifying points in a graph with corresponding values in a table and interpreting the numerical information in terms of the situation the graph represents
- Comparing situations by describing differences in their graphs
- Describing the relative steepness of graphs or parts of graphs in terms of different rates of change
- Comparing tables, graphs, and situations of constant change with those of non-constant change

Using Tables and Graphs Using tables to represent change

Unit 9 Math Focus Points

- Interpreting numbers in a table in terms of the situation they represent
- Using tables to represent the relationship between two quantities in a situation of constant change

Linear Change Describing and representing a constant rate of change

Unit 9 Math Focus Points

- Describing the relationship between two quantities in a situation of constant change, taking into account a beginning amount and a constant increase
- Creating a representation for a situation of constant change
- Finding the value of one quantity in a situation of constant change, given the value of the other
- Writing an arithmetic expression for finding the value of one quantity in terms of the other in a situation of constant change
- Making rules that relate one variable to another in situations of constant change
- Using symbolic letter notation to represent the value of one variable in terms of another

GRADE 4

Data and Probability

Data Analysis Representing Data

Unit 2 Math Focus Points

- Organizing ordered numerical data to describe a data set
- Using a line plot to represent ordered numerical data
- Representing two sets of data in order to compare them

Data Analysis Describing, summarizing, and comparing data

Unit 2 Math Focus Points

- Describing the shape of a data set: where the data are spread out or concentrated, what the highest and lowest values are, what the range is, and what the outliers are
- Determining the range of a data set

- Describing and interpreting data that compare two groups
- Describing what values are typical or atypical in a data set
- Comparing two sets of data using the shape and spread of the data
- Finding the median of a data set
- Using medians to compare groups
- Considering what information a median does and does not provide

Data Analysis Analyzing and interpreting data

Unit 2 Math Focus Points

- Drawing conclusions based on data
- Developing arguments based on the data

Data Analysis Designing and carrying out a data investigation

Unit 2 Math Focus Points

- Recording and keeping track of data
- Considering how well a data representation communicates to an audience
- Developing and revising a survey question

Probability Describing the probability of an event

Unit 2 Math Focus Points

- Associating the word *probability* with the likelihood of an event
- Arranging events along a line representing the range of *certain* to *impossible*
- Associating verbal descriptions of probability with numeric descriptions
- Using numbers from 0 to 1 as measures of probability
- Comparing the expected probability of an event with the actual results of repeated trials of that event

Geometry

Features of Shape Describing and classifying two-dimensional figures

Unit 4 Math Focus Points

- Defining polygons as closed figures with line segments as sides, and vertices
- Classifying polygons by attribute, including number of sides, length of sides, and size of angles
- Combining polygons to make new polygons
- Recognizing number of sides as a descriptor of various polygons
- Developing vocabulary to describe attributes and properties of quadrilaterals
- Understanding the relationship between squares and rectangles
- Making designs with mirror symmetry

Features of Shape Describing and measuring angles

Unit 4 Math Focus Points

- Identifying a right angle as 90 degrees
- Measuring acute angles by relating them to 90 degrees
- Using known angles to find the measure of other angles

Features of Shape Describing properties of three-dimensional shapes

Unit 7 Math Focus Points

- Describing attributes of geometric solids
- Naming geometric solids

Features of Shape Translating between two-dimensional and three-dimensional shapes

Unit 7 Math Focus Points

- Understanding how 3-D solids project silhouettes with 2-D shapes (for example, how a cone can produce both triangular and circular silhouettes)
- Decomposing images of 3-D shapes and then recombining them to make a given structure
- Visualizing what 3-D figures look like from different perspectives
- Recognizing how components of 3-D cube buildings come together to form the whole building
- Drawing silhouettes of 3-D cube buildings from different perspectives
- Integrating different silhouettes of an object, both to form a mental model and to build the whole object

GRADE 4

Measurement

Linear Measurement Measuring with standard units

Unit 2 Math Focus Points

- Using U.S. standard units to measure lengths longer than the measuring tool

Unit 4 Math Focus Points

- Reviewing the lengths of units of measure (inches, feet, yards, centimeters, meters)
- Using U.S. standard and metric units to accurately measure length
- Estimating lengths based on common units (centimeter, inch, foot, yard, meter)
- Determining when estimates or exact measurements are needed
- Finding perimeter using standard units

- Recognizing and explaining possible sources of measurement error
- Comparing different paths that have the same length

Unit 9 Math Focus Points

- Measuring in centimeters

Area Measurement Finding and understanding area

Unit 4 Math Focus Points

- Finding the area of symmetrical designs
- Understanding that the larger the unit of area, the smaller the number of units needed to measure the area
- Dividing irregular polygons into two shapes that have equal area
- Finding the area of polygons by decomposing shapes
- Finding the area of polygons using square units
- Finding the area of rectangles
- Finding the area of triangles in relation to the area of rectangles

Volume Structuring rectangular prisms and determining their volume

Unit 7 Math Focus Points

- Seeing that cubes filling a rectangular prism can be decomposed into congruent layers
- Finding the volume of cube buildings
- Designing patterns for boxes that hold a given number of cubes (volume)
- Developing a strategy for determining the volume of rectangular prisms
- Finding the number of cubes (volume) that will fit into the box made by a given pattern
- Doubling the number of cubes for a given box and considering how that changes the dimensions of the original box

GRADE 4

Ten-Minute Math

Closest Estimate

Units 8 and 9 Math Focus Points

◆ Approximating numbers to nearby landmark numbers,
  e.g., multiples of 10 or 100
◆ Calculating mentally
◆ Comparing answer choices to find the one closest to the actual
  answer

Counting Around the Class

Units 1, 3, and 8 Math Focus Points

◆ Finding the multiples of numbers through skip counting
◆ Becoming familiar with multiplication patterns
◆ Understanding the relationship between skip counting and
  multiplication

Practicing Place Value

Units 5, 6, and 7 Math Focus Points

◆ Reading and writing numbers up to 10,000
◆ Adding multiples of 10 to, and subtracting multiples of 10 from
  three- and four-digit numbers
◆ Reading and writing decimal fractions and decimal numbers
◆ Adding tenths and hundredths to, and subtracting them from
  decimal fractions and decimal numbers

Quick Images

Units 1, 4, and 7 Math Focus Points

◆ Organizing and analyzing visual images
◆ Developing language and concepts needed to communicate about
  spatial relationships
◆ Writing multiplication and division equations to represent the total
  number of shapes in a pattern
◆ Decomposing images of 2-D shapes and then recombining them to
  make a given design (Unit 4)
◆ Decomposing images of 3-D shapes and then recombining them to
  make a given structure (Unit 7)

Quick Survey

Units 2, 6, and 9 Math Focus Points

◆ Describing features of the data
◆ Interpreting and posing questions about the data

Today's Number

Units 1, 2, 4, and 5 Math Focus Points

◆ Generating equivalent expressions for a number using particular
  constraints
◆ Practicing computation skills
◆ Using notation to record expressions

GRADE 5

Number and Operations

Whole Number Operations **Reasoning about numbers and their factors**

Unit 1 Math Focus Points

- Determining whether one number is a factor or multiple of another
- Identifying prime, square, even and odd numbers
- Using known multiplication combinations to find equivalent multiplication combinations (e.g., $18 = 3 \times 6 = 3 \times (2 \times 3)$)
- Using known multiplication combinations to find multiplication combinations for numbers related by place value (e.g., $3 \times 6 = 18$; $3 \times 6 \times 10 = 180$)
- Finding all the ways to multiply whole numbers for a given product
- Finding all the factors of a number
- Using properties (even, odd, prime, square) and relationships (factor, multiple) of numbers to solve problems
- Determining the prime factorization of a number

Computational Fluency **Solving multiplication problems with 2-digit numbers**

Unit 1 Math Focus Points

- Solving 2-digit by 2-digit multiplication problems
- Describing and comparing strategies used to solve multiplication problems
- Breaking up multiplication problems efficiently
- Multiplying fluently by multiples of 10
- Estimating the product of two numbers
- Comparing multiplication problems to determine which product is greater
- Identifying and learning multiplication combinations ("facts") not yet known fluently
- Using clear and concise notation

Whole Number Operations **Understanding and using the relationship between multiplication and division to solve division problems**

Unit 1 Math Focus Points

- Solving division problems with 2-digit divisors
- Using knowledge of multiples of 10 to solve division problems
- Using and interpreting notation that represents division and relating division and multiplication notations (e.g., $170 \div 15 = $ ___ and ___ $\times 15 = 170$)
- Describing and comparing strategies used to solve division problems
- Comparing division problems to determine which quotient is greater
- Solving a division problem by breaking the dividend into parts

Unit 3 Math Focus Points

- Solving division problems related to the multiplication combinations to 12×12 (the division "facts", e.g., $64 \div 8$, $54 \div 6$) with fluency

Whole Number Operations **Representing the meaning of multiplication and division**

Unit 1 Math Focus Points

- Writing multiplication equations that describe dot arrangements
- Using arrays to model multiplication
- Representing a multiplication or division problem with a picture or diagram
- Creating a story problem represented by a multiplication or division expression
- Making sense of remainders in terms of problem contexts

Unit 7 Math Focus Points

- Representing equivalent expressions in multiplication
- Representing equivalent expressions in division
- Representing a division problem with a picture or diagram
- Creating a story context for a division expression

Whole Number Operations Reasoning about equivalent expressions in multiplication and division

Unit 7 Math Focus Points

- Generating equivalent multiplication expressions by doubling (or tripling) one factor and dividing the other by 2 (or 3)
- Developing arguments about how to generate equivalent expressions in multiplication
- Using story contexts and representations to support explanations of the relationship between equivalent expressions
- Generating equivalent division expressions
- Comparing equivalent multiplication expressions to equivalent division expressions

Computational Fluency Solving multiplication problems with 2-digit and 3-digit numbers

Unit 7 Math Focus Points

- Describing and comparing strategies used to solve multidigit multiplication problems
- Solving 2-digit by 2-digit or 3-digit multiplication problems fluently
- Estimating answers to multiplication and division problems
- Understanding the U.S. algorithm for multiplication

Computational Fluency Solving division problems with 2-digit divisors

Unit 7 Math Focus Points

- Solving division problems with a 2-digit divisor fluently
- Describing and comparing strategies used to solve division problems

The Base-Ten Number System Extending knowledge of the number system to 100,000 and beyond

Unit 3 Math Focus Points

- Reading, writing, and sequencing numbers to 10,000 and 100,000
- Understanding the place-value relationships between 10, 100, 1,000, and 10,000
- Learning the names of places larger than 100,000: million, billion, trillion

Computational Fluency Adding and subtracting accurately and efficiently

Unit 3 Math Focus Points

- Adding and subtracting multiples of 100 and 1,000
- Finding the difference between a number and 10,000
- Finding combinations of 3-digit numbers that add to 1,000
- Solving addition and subtraction problems with large numbers by focusing on the place value of the digits
- Solving whole-number addition and subtraction problems efficiently
- Using clear and concise notation for recording addition and subtraction strategies
- Interpreting and solving multistep problems
- Using story contexts and representations, such as number lines, to explain and justify solutions to subtraction problems

Unit 7 Math Focus Points

- Using clear and concise notation
- Solving multistep word problems
- Using all four operations to solve problems

Whole Number Operations Examining and using strategies for subtracting whole numbers

Unit 3 Math Focus Points

- Identifying, describing, and comparing subtraction strategies by focusing on how each strategy starts
- Analyzing and using different subtraction strategies
- Developing arguments about how the differences represented by two subtraction expressions are related (e.g., 1,208 − 297 and 1,208 − 300)
- Understanding the meaning of the steps and notation of the U.S. algorithm for subtraction

Rational Numbers Understanding the meaning of fractions and percents

Unit 4 Math Focus Points

- Interpreting everyday uses of fractions, decimals, and percents
- Finding fractional parts of a whole or of a group (of objects, people, and so on)
- Finding fractional parts of a rectangular area
- Representing fractions on a number line
- Finding a percentage of a group (of objects, people, and so on)
- Finding a percentage of a rectangular area
- Identifying fraction and percent equivalents through reasoning about representations and known equivalents and relationships
- Interpreting the meaning of the numerator and denominator of a fraction
- Using equivalent fractions and percents to solve problems

Rational Numbers Comparing fractions

Unit 4 Math Focus Points

- Ordering fractions and justifying their order through reasoning about fraction equivalents and relationships
- Comparing fractions and percents to the landmarks 0, $\frac{1}{2}$, and 1
- Finding and comparing fractional parts and percents of a whole or a group
- Comparing fractional parts of different-sized wholes
- Using equivalencies to place fractions on a set of number lines (fraction tracks)
- Comparing fractions on a number line
- Ordering mixed numbers and fractions greater than 1

Rational Numbers Understanding the meaning of decimal fractions

Unit 6 Math Focus Points

- Identifying everyday uses of fractions and decimals
- Representing decimal fractions as parts of an area
- Reading and writing tenths, hundredths, and thousandths
- Identifying decimal, fraction, and percent equivalents
- Representing decimals using a number line
- Interpreting fractions as division
- Interpreting the meaning of digits in a decimal number

Rational Numbers Comparing decimal fractions

Unit 6 Math Focus Points

◆ Ordering decimals and justifying their order through reasoning about decimal representations, equivalents, and relationships

◆ Comparing decimals to the landmarks $0, \frac{1}{2},$ and 1

Computation with Rational Numbers Adding and subtracting fractions

Unit 4 Math Focus Points

◆ Finding fractional parts of the rotation around a circle

◆ Adding fractions by using a rotation model

◆ Adding and subtracting fractions through reasoning about fraction equivalents and relationships

◆ Adding and subtracting fractions using a number line

◆ Finding combinations of fractions with sums between 0 and 2

Computation with Rational Numbers Adding decimals

Unit 6 Math Focus Points

◆ Estimating sums of decimal numbers

◆ Using representations to add tenths, hundredths, and thousandths

◆ Adding decimals to the thousandths through reasoning about place value, equivalents, and representations

Patterns, Functions, and Change

Using Tables and Graphs Using tables to represent change

Unit 8 Math Focus Point

◆ Using tables to represent the relationship between two quantities

Using Tables and Graphs Using graphs to represent change

Unit 8 Math Focus Points

◆ Plotting points on a coordinate grid to represent a situation in which one quantity is changing in relation to another

◆ Identifying points in a graph with corresponding values in a table and interpreting the numerical information in terms of the situation the graph represents

◆ Describing the relative steepness of graphs or parts of graphs in terms of different rates of change

◆ Comparing situations by describing differences in their graphs

Linear Change Describing and representing situations with a constant rate of change

Unit 8 Math Focus Points

◆ Describing the relationship between two quantities in a situation with a constant rate of change, taking into account a beginning amount and a constant increase (or decrease)

◆ Finding the value of one quantity in a situation with a constant rate of change, given the value of the other (e.g., if you know the age, what is the height? or if you know the number of rows, what is the perimeter?)

◆ Writing an arithmetic expression for finding the value of one quantity in terms of the other in a situation with a constant rate of change

- Making rules that relate one variable to the other in situations with a constant rate of change
- Using symbolic letter notation to represent the value of one variable in terms of another variable

Nonlinear Change Describing and representing situations in which the change is not constant

Unit 8 Math Focus Points

- Comparing tables, graphs, and situations with a constant rate of change with those in which the rate of change is not constant
- Describing a situation in which the rate of change is not constant but can be determined
- Describing how a graph represents a situation in which the rate of change is not constant

GRADE 5

Data and Probability

Data Analysis Representing data

Unit 9 Math Focus Points

- Using a line plot to represent ordered, numerical data
- Representing two sets of data in order to compare them
- Considering how well a data representation communicates to an audience

Data Analysis Describing, summarizing, and comparing data

Unit 9 Math Focus Points

- Comparing sets of data using the shape and spread of the data

- Describing the shape of a set of data: where the data are concentrated, the median, what is typical, highest and lowest values, range and outliers
- Using medians to compare groups

Data Analysis Analyzing and interpreting data

Unit 9 Math Focus Points

- Developing arguments based on data
- Drawing conclusions based on data
- Considering how well conclusions are supported by data

Data Analysis Designing and carrying out a data investigation

Unit 9 Math Focus Points

- Designing an experiment to answer a question about two groups, objects, or conditions
- Developing and carrying out consistent procedures for collecting data from an experiment
- Recording and keeping track of a set of data
- Carrying out multiple trials in an experiment

Probability Describing the probability of an event

Unit 9 Math Focus Points

- Comparing the expected probability of an event with the actual results of repeated trials of that event
- Using numbers from 0 to 1 as measures of probability
- Determining the fairness of a game based on the probability of winning for each player

GRADE 5

Geometry

Features of Shape **Translating between two-dimensional and three-dimensional shapes**

Unit 2 Math Focus Point

◆ Decomposing 3-D shapes and then recombining them to make a given building

Features of Shape **Describing and classifying two-dimensional figures**

Unit 5 Math Focus Points

◆ Identifying attributes of polygons
◆ Describing triangles by the sizes of their angles and the lengths of their sides
◆ Using attributes to describe and compare quadrilaterals including parallelograms, rectangles, rhombuses, and squares
◆ Defining a regular polygon as a polygon with all sides and all angles equal

Features of Shape **Describing and measuring angles**

Unit 5 Math Focus Point

◆ Using known angles to find the measures of other angles

Features of Shape **Creating and describing similar shapes**

Unit 5 Math Focus Points

◆ Recognizing and building similar figures
◆ Examining the relationship among angles, line lengths, and areas of similar polygons
◆ Making a generalization about the changes in area of similar figures

◆ Building similar figures for polygons made from two or more Power Polygon pieces
◆ Using Power Polygons to find the areas of similar hexagons

GRADE 5

Measurement

Linear and Area Measurement **Finding perimeter and area of rectangles**

Unit 5 Math Focus Points

◆ Comparing the perimeters and areas of rectangles when the dimensions are multiplied by given amounts
◆ Using numerical and/or geometric patterns to describe how the perimeters and areas of rectangles change when the dimensions change
◆ Using representations to explain how perimeters and areas of rectangles change
◆ Creating different rectangles with the same area but different perimeters
◆ Understanding square units as a unit of measure
◆ Creating different rectangles with the same perimeter but different areas
◆ Describing the shapes of rectangles that have the same area or the same perimeter

Unit 8 Math Focus Points

◆ Measuring length with meters and centimeters
◆ Finding the perimeter of a rectangle
◆ Finding the area of a rectangle

Volume Structuring rectangular prisms and determining their volume

Unit 2 Math Focus Points

- Determining the number of cubes that will fit into the box made by a given pattern
- Developing a strategy for determining the volume of rectangular prisms
- Designing patterns for boxes that hold a given number of cubes
- Finding the volume of rectangular prisms
- Considering how the dimensions of a box change when the volume is changed (doubled, halved, or tripled)
- Organizing rectangular packages to fit in rectangular boxes
- Designing a box that can be completely filled with several differently-shaped rectangular packages
- Determining the volume, in cubic centimeters, of a small prism
- Constructing units of volume—cubic centimeter, cubic inch, cubic foot, cubic yard (optional), cubic meter
- Choosing an appropriate unit of volume to measure a large space
- Finding the volume of a large space, such as the classroom, using cubic meters
- Describing and defending measurement methods
- Building rectangular solids

Volume Structuring prisms, pyramids, cylinders, and cones and determining their volume

Unit 2 Math Focus Points

- Comparing volumes of differently-shaped containers
- Building rectangular solids
- Finding volume relationships between solids, particularly those with the same base and height
- Building a prism with three times the volume of a given pyramid
- Demonstrating the 3:1 relationship between rectangular prisms and pyramids with the same base and height
- Finding volume, in cubic centimeters, of prisms, pyramids, cylinders, and cones

GRADE 5

Ten-Minute Math

Estimation and Number Sense

Units 2–4 and 6–9 Math Focus Points

- Estimating solutions to 2- and 3-digit multiplication and division problems
- Estimating solutions to 4- and 5-digit addition and subtraction problems
- Breaking apart, reordering, or changing numbers mentally to determine a reasonable estimate

Guess My Rule

Unit 4 Math Focus Points

- Identifying fractions of a group
- Using evidence and formulating questions to make hypotheses about the common characteristics in a group
- Systematically eliminating possibilities

Number Puzzles

Units 1 and 7 Math Focus Points

◆ Identifying prime, square, even, and odd numbers

◆ Determining if one number is a factor or multiple of another

Practicing Place Value

Units 3, 6, and 8 Math Focus Points

◆ Recognizing and interpreting the value of each digit in 4- and 5-digit numbers

◆ Finding different combinations of a number, using only 1,000s, 100s, 10s, and 1s and recognizing their equivalency (i.e., 1 hundred, 3 tens, and 7 ones = 12 tens and 17 ones, etc.)

◆ Reading and writing numbers up to 100,000

◆ Adding multiples of 10 to, and subtracting multiples of 10 from 4- and 5-digit numbers

◆ Reading and writing decimal fractions and decimal numbers

◆ Adding tenths or hundredths to, and subtracting them from, decimal fractions and decimal numbers

Quick Images

Units 1, 2, and 5 Math Focus Points

◆ Organizing and analyzing visual images

◆ Developing language and concepts needed to communicate about spatial relationships

◆ Writing multiplication and division equations to represent the total number of shapes in a pattern

◆ Decomposing images of 2-D shapes and then recombining them to make a given design (Unit 2)

◆ Decomposing images of 3-D shapes and then recombining them to make a given structure (Unit 5)

Quick Survey

Units 5 and 9 Math Focus Points

◆ Describing features of the data

◆ Interpreting and posing questions about the data

NCTM Curriculum Focal Points and Connections

The set of three curriculum focal points and related connections for mathematics in Grade 5 follow. These topics are the recommended content emphases for this grade level. It is essential that these focal points be addressed in contexts that promote problem solving, reasoning, communication, making connections, and designing and analyzing representations.

Grade 5 Curriculum Focal Points	*Investigations* Units
Number and Operations and ***Algebra:*** **Developing an understanding of and fluency with division of whole numbers** Students apply their understanding of models for division, place value, properties, and the relationship of division to multiplication as they develop, discuss, and use efficient, accurate, and generalizable procedures to find quotients involving multidigit dividends. They select appropriate methods and apply them accurately to estimate quotients or calculate them mentally, depending on the context and numbers involved. They develop fluency with efficient procedures, including the standard algorithm, for dividing whole numbers, understand why the procedures work (on the basis of place value and properties of operations), and use them to solve problems. They consider the context in which a problem is situated to select the most useful form of the quotient for the solution, and they interpret it appropriately.	**Addressed in the work of:** • *Number Puzzles and Multiple Towers* (Multiplication and Division 1) • *How Many People? How Many Teams?* (Multiplication and Division 2) • Ten-Minute Math: Estimation and Number Sense: *Closest Estimate, Quick Images: Seeing Numbers* **Also supported in the work of:** • *Growth Patterns* (Patterns, Function, and Change)
Number and Operations: **Developing an understanding of and fluency with addition and subtraction of fractions and decimals** Students apply their understandings of fractions and fraction models to represent the addition and subtraction of fractions with unlike denominators as equivalent calculations with like denominators. They apply their understandings of decimal models, place value, and properties to add and subtract decimals. They develop fluency with standard procedures for adding and subtracting fractions and decimals. They make reasonable estimates of fraction and decimal sums and differences. Students add and subtract fractions and decimals to solve problems, including problems involving measurement.	**Addressed in the work of:** • *What's That Portion* (Fractions and Percents 1) • *Decimals on Grids and Number Lines* (Decimals, Fractions, and Percents 2) • Ten-Minute Math: Estimation and Number Sense: *Closest Estimate, Practicing Place Value* **Also supported in the work of:** • *How Long Can You Stand on One Foot?* (Data Analysis and Probability)
Geometry and ***Measurement*** and ***Algebra:*** **Describing three-dimensional shapes and analyzing their properties, including volume and surface area** Students relate two-dimensional shapes to three-dimensional shapes and analyze properties of polyhedral solids, describing them by the number of edges, faces, or vertices as well as the types of faces. Students recognize volume as an attribute of three-dimensional space. They understand that they can quantify volume by finding the total number of same-sized units of volume that they need to fill the space without gaps or overlaps. They understand that a cube that is 1 unit on an edge is the standard unit for measuring volume. They select appropriate units, strategies, and tools for solving problems that involve estimating or measuring volume. They decompose three-dimensional shapes and find surface areas and volumes of prisms. As they work with surface area, they find and justify relationships among the formulas for the areas of different polygons. They measure necessary attributes of shapes to use area formulas to solve problems.	**Addressed in the work of:** • *Prisms and Pyramids* (3-D Geometry and Measurement) • Ten-Minute Math: *Quick Images: 3D* **Also supported in the work of:** • *Measuring Polygons* (2-D Geometry and Measurement)

Connections to the Focal Points	Investigations Units
Algebra: Students use patterns, models, and relationships as contexts for writing and solving simple equations and inequalities. They create graphs of simple equations. They explore prime and composite numbers and discover concepts related to the addition and subtraction of fractions as they use factors and multiples, including applications of common factors and common multiples. They develop an understanding of the order of operations and use it for all operations.	**Addressed in the work of:** • *Growth Patterns* (Patterns, Function, and Change) • *Number Puzzles and Multiple Towers* (Multiplication and Division 1) • *How Many People? How Many Teams?* (Multiplication and Division 2) • *What's That Portion* (Fractions and Percents 1) • *Decimals on Grids and Number Lines* (Decimals, Fractions, and Percents 2) • Ten-Minute Math: *Number Puzzles, Quick Images: Seeing Numbers*
Measurement: Students' experiences connect their work with solids and volume to their earlier work with capacity and weight or mass. They solve problems that require attention to both approximation and precision of measurement.	**Addressed in the work of:** • *Prisms and Pyramids* (3-D Geometry and Measurement) **Also supported in the work of:** • *Measuring Polygons* (2-D Geometry and Measurement)
Data Analysis: Students apply their understanding of whole numbers, fractions, and decimals as they construct and analyze double-bar and line graphs and use ordered pairs on coordinate grids.	**Addressed in the work of:** • *How Long Can You Stand on One Foot?* (Data Analysis and Probability) • *Growth Patterns* (Patterns, Function, and Change) • Ten-Minute Math: *Quick Surveys, Guess My Rule* **Also supported in the work of:** • *What's That Portion* (Fractions and Percents 1) • *Decimals on Grids and Number Lines* (Decimals, Fractions, and Percents 2)
Number and Operations: Building on their work in Grade 4, students extend their understanding of place value to numbers through millions and millionths in various contexts. They apply what they know about multiplication of whole numbers to larger numbers. Students also explore contexts that they can describe with negative numbers (e.g., situations of owing money or measuring elevations above and below sea level.)	**Addressed in the work of:** • *Number Puzzles and Multiple Towers* (Multiplication and Division 1) • *How Many People? How Many Teams?* (Multiplication and Division 2) • *Thousands of Miles, Thousands of Seats* (Addition, Subtraction, and the Number System) • Ten-Minute Math: *Practicing Place Value, Estimation and Number Sense, Quick Images: Seeing Numbers*

Each entry is identified by the Curriculum Unit number (in yellow) and its page number(s).

Grade 5 Curriculum Units

U1 Number Puzzles and Multiple Towers
U2 Prisms and Pyramids
U3 Thousands of Miles, Thousands of Seats
U4 What's That Portion?
U5 Measuring Polygons
U6 Decimals on Grids and Number Lines
U7 How Many People? How Many Teams?
U8 Growth Patterns
U9 How Long Can You Stand on One Foot?

A

Adding by place strategy, U6: 95, 101, 104, 113–114, 144
Adding up strategy, U3: 16–17, 34–35, 59, 70, 106, 120–121, 124, 140
Adding zero strategy, U1: 86–87, 181
Addition. *See also* Sum.
  comparison problems, U3: 16
  of decimals, U6: 10, 12, 87–91, 93–95, 99–101, 103–106, 108–111, 113–114, 132–133, 142–144
  distance problems, U3: 66–68, 80, 84
  of fractions, U4: 10–12, 95–96, 98–100, 102–106, 108–111, 122–126, 129–134, 136–138, 140–141, 160–161
  missing parts problems, U3: 16
  of multiples of 100 and 1,000, U3: 11, 33–35, 37–40
  notation for, U3: 38, 65–66
  of percents, U4: 10–11
  related problems, U3: 45–48, 52
  relationship to subtraction, U3: 16–17, 37
  strategies for, U3: 90, 95–96, 98–99, 116–117
  strategies for decimals, U6: 95, 101, 104, 113–114, 132–133, 143–144
  strategies for fractions, U4: 137–138
  U.S. Algorithm for, U3: 12, 128–130
  with very large numbers, U3: 94–96, 98–103, 116–118
Algorithms. *See* U.S. Conventional Algorithms.
Angles
  acute, U5: 27
  exterior/interior, U5: 53, 60
  measuring by comparison, U5: 11, 51–54, 58–59, 64, 163–164
  obtuse, U5: 27
  of regular polygons, U5: 46–49, 152
  right (90°), U5: 25
  of similar polygons, U5: 112–113, 152
  supplementary, U5: 36–38, 42–43, 49, 142

Area
  change in, U8: 67–71, 90–96
  compared to perimeter, U5: 72–75, 80–82, 84–85
  dimensions and, U5: 72–75, 77–78, 80–82, 84–88, 112, 125–126, 127–128, 165–166
  of hexagons, U5: 115–116, 126–127, 130–131
  of rectangles, U5: 11, 84–85, 86–88, 90–93, 96–99, 101–104
  relationship to perimeter, U8: 14, 69–74, 76–81, 83–88, 93
  of similar polygons, U5: 112–113, 125–128
  of squares, U5: 72–75, 77–78, 80–82, 86–88; U8: 103–106, 130–132
Arguments, U9: 11, 36–37, 39–40, 44–45
Arithmetic expressions. *See also* Notation. U8: 14, 47, 53, 72–73, 77, 79, 83–84, 98, 104
Arrays
  area of, U2: 113–114, 133–134; U8: 14, 67–74, 76–81, 83–88, 90–96, 103–105, 130–132
  building, U1: 28–35
  dimensions of, U1: 32, 156–157
  labeling, U1: 158
  number puzzles, U1: 34–35
  perimeter of, U8: 11, 13–14, 18, 69–74, 76–81, 83–88, 92–96, 120–121, 138–139
  of primes and squares, U1: 37–38
  representation of multiplication, U1: 12–13, 71–76, 80–83, 156–158, 172
  unmarked, U1: 32, 159–160
  volume of, U2: 27, 32
Associative property of multiplication, U1: 87, 154
Attributes of polygons, U5: 10, 25–29, 32–35, 43–44, 137–138
Attributes of polyhedra, U2: 126

B

Bar graphs. *See* Graphs.
Bases, U2: 96
Base-ten number system. *See also* Decimals; Place value. U3: 10–11, 113–114; U6: 10, 123–124
Billion, U3: 11, 53
Boxes, U2: 10–11, 27–30, 59–60, 84–86, 121–122
Breaking apart by place value strategy, U7: 56, 59–60
Breaking fractions apart strategy, U4: 37, 45, 72, 138
Breaking numbers apart strategy, U1: 71–73, 75–76, 81–83, 98, 101–104, 117, 140, 161, 170, 172, 181, 183–184, 186–189; U2: 42–43; U3: 45–48, 116–117, 123–124, 140–141; U6: 95; U7: 11–13, 16–17, 49–51, 56, 59
Breaking the dividend apart strategy, U7: 12, 70, 125, 148–149

C

Categorical data. *See* Data.
Changing numbers to make an easier problem strategy, U1: 73, 75, 117, 161–162, 183; U2: 43; U3: 12, 17–18, 60, 70, 72–74, 107–108, 117, 120–121, 141; U6: 104, 114; U7: 12, 49–51, 70, 124
Classifying polygons, U5: 10, 27–30, 32–33, 40–42, 43–44, 46–49, 59, 63–64, 137–138
Cluster problems, U1: 91–99, 136–140, 143, 148, 165
Common denominators, U4: 100, 161

of predictable but not constant change, U8: 57–60, 103–105, 108–110

predicting other situations based on, U8: 94

representing change with, U8: 120–123

representing non-constant rate of change, 29–32, 34–40, 116, 121–123

slope (steepness), U8: 11–12, 19, 39, 100–101, 121

of staircase tower growth, U8: 108–110, 131

of whole number situations, U8: 84

y-intercept, U8: 19

line plots, U5: 71; U8: 115; U9: 10, 25–26, 31, 66, 69–70, 90, 94–96, 113

Greater than (>), U1: 88

H

Halves, U4: 28–30, 47–49, 59–61, 71–75, 77, 82–84, 86, 95, 102–106, 111, 113–115, 117–120, 122–126, 129–134, 136, 140–141, 153, 172–173; U6: 67–68

Halving strategy, U4: 38

Height, U2: 127; U8: 27–32, 34–40

Heptagon, U5: 47

Hexagons, U5: 47, 115–116, 120–122, 127, 130–131, 167–169

Horizontal axis line, U9: 69

Hundredths, U6: 11, 32–36, 39–41, 50–53, 57, 78

I

Independent variables. *See* Variables.

J

Justification. *See also* Proofs. U3: 19, 125–127; U7: 10–11, 18, 28–31, 33–36, 39–40, 119–122; U9: 36–37, 108

"Just know" strategy, U4: 84

K

Known combination strategy, U7: 12

Known equivalents strategy, U4: 38, 42–43, 45, 64–69, 72, 83–84, 109, 131, 137, 161

L

Landmarks, U1: 124; U3: 29–30, 98; U4: 11, 152–153; U6: 11–12, 25, 40–41

Layer strategy, U2: 34–35, 133–134

Less than (<), U1: 88

Linear functions. *See also* Rate of change.

comparing different situations, U8: 52–55, 122–123, 137–138

comparing to non-linear functions, U8: 10–11, 14, 59–60, 99–101, 122–123

representations of, U8: 12–14, 44–48, 50–55, 83–88, 90–96, 98–101, 116, 118–119, 121–123, 137–138

Line graphs. *See* Graphs.

Line plot. *See* Graphs.

***LogoPaths* Software,** U2: 13; U3: 13; U4: 13; U5: 36–38, 42–43, 49, 54–56, 60–61, 64, 79–80, 99, 101, 116–119, 122–123, 127, 132, 139–142; U6: 13; U8: 15; U9: 13

Angle and Turn, U5: 36–38, 42, 49

commands of, U5: 37, 43, 55, 60, 79–80, 140, 142

mathematics of, U5: 141

Polygon Pairs, U5: 116–119, 122–123, 127, 132

Rhombuses and Parallelograms (Free Explore), U5: 54–56, 79–80, 99, 101

Triangles (Free Explore), U5: 54–56, 60–61, 64

M

Maximum/minimum values. *See* Values.

Measurement, U2: 11, 74–76, 78–82, 106–109, 123–124; U8: 27–29

Median, U9: 11, 31–33, 38, 44, 113, 117–118

Metric system. *See* Units of measure.

Million, U3: 11, 53

Minimum/maximum values, U9: 27–28, 31–33, 38, 43, 44, 91, 113

Missing parts problems, U3: 16–17, 66–68

Mixed numbers, U4: 11, 119, 137–138, 140

Mode, U9: 33, 44, 113–114

Money, U3: 18; U4: 42

Multiples, U1: 11, 13, 33–35, 39–40, 120–125, 131–133; U2: 42–43; U3: 44–48, 52, 95, 137–139

Multiples of ten strategy, U7: 73, 89, 95

Multiplication. *See also* Products. U7: 44

by 10s, U1: 13, 86–87

2-digit by 2-digit numbers, U1: 11–12, 100–107

associative property of, U1: 87

cluster problems, U1: 91–99, 165

combinations, U1: 32, 45–51, 62–64, 115

distributive property of, U1: 12, 16, 83; U7: 11–12, 16–18

equivalent expressions, U7: 10, 16, 27–31, 33–36, 38–40, 144–145

estimating answers, U1: 89–90; U7: 54–56

factors, U1: 10–11, 30, 33, 39–40, 49–51, 54–55, 58, 59–64, 153–154

with large numbers, U7: 112, 115–116

with more than 2 numbers, U1: 48–51, 181–182

prime factorization and, U1: 10, 49–51, 61–64

relationship to division, U1: 12–13, 18–19, 115, 131–135, 169; U7: 70

representations of, U1: 31–35, 71–84, 156–160

starter problems, U1: 106, 171

strategies for, U1: 70–76, 81–83, 86–87, 98, 101–104, 117, 161–162, 171–173, 181, 183–184; U2: 42–43; U7: 11, 16–18, 27–31, 33–36, 39–40, 49–51, 56, 59, 119–121

U.S. Conventional Algorithms, U7: 12, 59–61, 127–129, 146–147

Grade 5 Curriculum Units

U1 Number Puzzles and Multiple Towers
U2 Prisms and Pyramids
U3 Thousands of Miles, Thousands of Seats
U4 What's That Portion?
U5 Measuring Polygons
U6 Decimals on Grids and Number Lines
U7 How Many People? How Many Teams?
U8 Growth Patterns
U9 How Long Can You Stand on One Foot?

Grade 5 Curriculum Units

U1 Number Puzzles and Multiple Towers
U2 Prisms and Pyramids
U3 Thousands of Miles, Thousands of Seats
U4 What's That Portion?
U5 Measuring Polygons
U6 Decimals on Grids and Number Lines
U7 How Many People? How Many Teams?
U8 Growth Patterns
U9 How Long Can You Stand on One Foot?

Grade 5 Curriculum Units

U1 Number Puzzles and Multiple Towers
U2 Prisms and Pyramids
U3 Thousands of Miles, Thousands of Seats
U4 What's That Portion?
U5 Measuring Polygons
U6 Decimals on Grids and Number Lines
U7 How Many People? How Many Teams?
U8 Growth Patterns
U9 How Long Can You Stand on One Foot?